D1130118

LECTURES ON THE NUMERICAL SOLUTION OF LINEAR, SINGULAR, AND NONLINEAR DIFFERENTIAL EQUATIONS

DONALD GREENSPAN

Computer Center and Computer Sciences Department
University of Michigan

PRENTICE-HALL, INC.

ENGLEWOOD CLIFFS, N.J.

PRENTICE-HALL INTERNATIONAL, INC., *London*
PRENTICE-HALL OF AUSTRALIA, PTY. LTD., *Sydney*
PRENTICE-HALL OF CANADA, LTD., *Toronto*
PRENTICE-HALL OF INDIA PRIVATE, LTD., *New Delhi*
PRENTICE-HALL OF JAPAN, INC., *Tokyo*

Current printing (last digit):

10 9 8 7 6 5 4 3 2 1

Library of Congress Catalog Card Number: 68-54569

Printed in the United States of America

PREFACE

Annually, for several years, I have had the privilege of delivering ten lectures on numerical methods and applications at summer conferences at the University of Michigan. From year to year the lectures have changed in order to reflect the most recent developments in the field. By 1968, progress in the application of digital computers to both scientific and technological problems had become so startling, and the fields of application so diversified, that I felt the time was appropriate for organizing and presenting the material as a monograph.

The problems to be studied here are either boundary value problems or initial value problems which can be reformulated as boundary value problems. The techniques developed are boundary value techniques which utilize finite differences. And the entire development is of such a nature that the methods described can be programmed easily for any digital computer.

The book is essentially a survey approach. Scientists and technologists should be able to determine easily from the text what the latest methods are and whether those methods apply to their problems. The extensive bibliography renders the supporting mathematical theories accessible to mathematicians and numerical analysts. Study of the references inserted throughout the text will enable teachers to adapt the material for classroom presentation.

DONALD GREENSPAN

CONTENTS

Lecture 1. MATHEMATICAL PRELIMINARIES 1

Lecture 2. NUMERICAL SOLUTION OF THE INTERIOR AND THE EXTERIOR DIRICHLET PROBLEMS 22

Lecture 3. NUMERICAL SOLUTION OF PROBLEMS FOR GENERAL LINEAR AND SINGULAR ELLIPTIC EQUATIONS 38

Lecture 4. LINEAR PROBLEMS IN THREE DIMENSIONS AND THE CLASSICAL PROBLEM OF CAPACITY 52

Lecture 5. MILDLY NONLINEAR ELLIPTIC PROBLEMS 65

Lecture 6. MILDLY NONLINEAR PARABOLIC PROBLEMS 73

Lecture 7. MILDLY NONLINEAR HYPERBOLIC PROBLEMS 85

Lecture 8. APPROXIMATE EXTREMIZATIONS OF FUNCTIONALS 96

Lecture 9. NONLINEAR PROBLEMS 108

Lecture 10. STEADY STATE NAVIER STOKES PROBLEMS 122

BIBLIOGRAPHY 148

Lecture 1 - Mathematical Preliminaries

1.1. Introduction. One of the great disappointments in the development of modern mathematics is that it has provided the engineer and scientist with no general analytical method for solving nonlinear differential equations. Indeed, at a time when such precise instruments of measurement like the electron microscope and atomic clock are indicating with no uncertainty that the nonlinear model is more often the rule rather than the exception, analytical mathematical methods are restricted to questions of existence, uniqueness, and stability.

This situation has been brightened considerably by the development of the high speed digital computer and by the concomitant revitalization and growth of the study of numerical methods, and it is to such methods that we shall direct our attention.

Our study will begin with linear problems and will lead gradually through mildly nonlinear problems to highly nonlinear ones.
Though emphasis will be laid on partial differential equations, it is important to realize that all results and techniques specialize to ordinary differential equations. And finally note that although we shall treat elliptic, parabolic and hyperbolic problems, our stress on boundary value techniques will have particular value for elliptic differential equations, for which boundary value problems are most natural.

Throughout the lectures all functions and all variables will be limited to the real domain.

<u>1. 2. The Generalized Newton's Method.</u> It will be necessary for us to be able to solve large systems of linear and nonlinear algebraic and transcendental systems of equations. For the systems to be considered in these lectures, the generalized Newton's method, to be developed next, will suffice completely.

Suppose first that one wishes to find a root of the equation

$$f(x) = 0, \tag{1.1}$$

where f is a given differentiable function. Let the graph of

$$y = f(x) \tag{1.2}$$

be as shown in Figure 1. 1. The problem of finding a root of (1. 1) is, of course, completely equivalent to that of finding a zero of (1. 2), that is, of finding a point where the graph of (1. 2) intersects the X-axis, and we shall try to do the latter as follows.

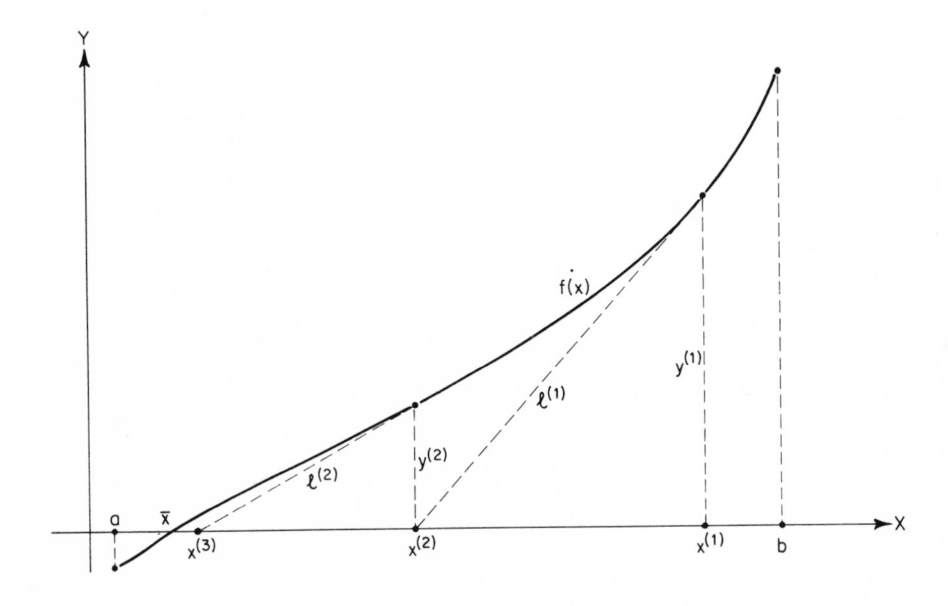

Figure 1.1

Suppose that $\bar{x}$, as shown in Figure 1.1, is a zero of $f(x)$. Since $\bar{x}$ is, in general, not known, let us make a guess at it (called an initial guess), say, $x = x^{(1)}$. If $f(x^{(1)}) = 0$, then the problem is solved. In all probability, however, $f(x^{(1)}) \neq 0$, and one proceeds as follows to try to get a new value $x^{(2)}$ which approximates $\bar{x}$ better than does $x^{(1)}$. Let $f(x^{(1)}) = y^{(1)}$. Then, at the point $(x^{(1)}, y^{(1)})$, the slope of the tangent line $\ell^{(1)}$ to $f(x)$ is $f'(x^{(1)})$. Thus, the equation of the line $\ell^{(1)}$ is

$$y - f(x^{(1)}) = f'(x^{(1)}) \cdot (x - x^{(1)}). \tag{1.3}$$

Let $x^{(2)}$ be the point in which $\ell^{(1)}$ intersects the X-axis. Analytically $x^{(2)}$ can be determined from (1.3) by setting $y = 0$, that is, from

$$-f(x^{(1)}) = f'(x^{(1)}) \cdot (x^{(2)} - x^{(1)}). \tag{1.4}$$

Under the assumption that $f'(x^{(1)}) \neq 0$, that is, that $\ell^{(1)}$ is not parallel to the X-axis, it follows from (1.4) that

$$x^{(2)} = x^{(1)} - \frac{f(x^{(1)})}{f'(x^{(1)})}. \tag{1.5}$$

If $f(x^{(2)}) = 0$, then the problem is solved. If $f(x^{(2)}) \neq 0$, then one proceeds to try to improve on the approximation $x^{(2)}$. Let $f(x^{(2)}) = y^{(2)}$. Let $\ell^{(2)}$ be the tangent line to $f(x)$ at $(x^{(2)}, y^{(2)})$. Let $x^{(3)}$ be the intersection of $\ell^{(2)}$ with the X-axis, so that, as in the derivation of (1.5), one finds

$$x^{(3)} = x^{(2)} - \frac{f(x^{(2)})}{f'(x^{(2)})}, \qquad f'(x^{(2)}) \neq 0. \tag{1.6}$$

Again, if $f(x^{(3)}) = 0$, then the problem is solved. If $f(x^{(3)}) \neq 0$, then proceed to construct $x^{(4)}, x^{(5)}, \ldots$, in the same spirit as $x^{(2)}$ and $x^{(3)}$ were constructed above. After n steps a value $x^{(n+1)}$ is determined by the formula

$$x^{(n+1)} = x^{(n)} - \frac{f(x^{(n)})}{f'(x^{(n)})}, \qquad f'(x^{(n)}) \neq 0 . \tag{1.7}$$

The formula (1.7) is called Newton's formula and the entire iterative procedure described above is called Newton's method.

Newton's method can be used under suitable conditions [328] to approximate a root quite accurately by hand, and, indeed, to almost any degree of accuracy with great speed on a digital computer.

Example 1. Approximate the positive root of the equation

$$x^3 + \sqrt{3}x^2 - 2x - 2\sqrt{3} = 0 \tag{1.8}$$

by Newton's method.

Solution. If one sets

$$f(x) = x^3 + \sqrt{3}\,x^2 - 2x - 2\sqrt{3}, \tag{1.9}$$

then

$$f(0) = -2\sqrt{3} < 0$$

$$f(1) = 1 + \sqrt{3} - 2 - 2\sqrt{3} = -1 - \sqrt{3} < 0$$

$$f(2) = 8 + 4\sqrt{3} - 4 - 2\sqrt{3} = 4 + 2\sqrt{3} > 0,$$

and a root of (1.8) lies between 1 and 2. Newton's formula has the form

(1.10) $$x^{(n+1)} = x^{(n)} - \frac{[x^{(n)}]^3 + \sqrt{3}[x^{(n)}]^2 - 2x^{(n)} - 2\sqrt{3}}{3[x^{(n)}]^2 + 2\sqrt{3}x^{(n)} - 2} .$$

Approximating $\sqrt{3}$ by 1.7, setting $x^{(1)} = 2.0$, and rounding to one decimal place, one has from (1.10) that

$$x^{(2)} \sim 1.6$$
$$x^{(3)} \sim 1.4$$
$$x^{(4)} \sim 1.4 ,$$

where the symbol $\sim$ is used to designate an approximate value. Since $x^{(3)} = x^{(4)}$, the Newton iteration formula will yield no new value of x and the approximation which results is $x \sim 1.4$. The exact solution is $x = \sqrt{2} \sim 1.414213562$.

Example 2. Newton's method was programmed for the CDC 3600 to find a positive root of (1.8). To make it difficult for the computer the initial guess was taken to be $x^{(1)} = 100000$ and numbers were rounded to nine decimal places. The iteration stopped with $x^{(32)} = x^{(33)} \sim 1.414213562$. The running time was 4 milliseconds.

For more difficult problems than those considered in the above examples, it will be of value to have a method which can yield a root in fewer iterations than those determined by Newton's method. Such a method can be developed as follows. Suppose, instead of constructing the line $\ell^{(1)}$ shown in Figure 1.1, one were clever enough to construct a different line through $(x^{(1)}, y^{(1)})$ which would intersect the X-axis closer to $\bar{x}$

than is $x^{(2)}$. Such a line would have an equation of the form

$$y - f(x^{(1)}) = \tau \cdot f'(x^{(1)}) \cdot (x - x^{(1)}), \qquad \tau \neq 1, \tag{1.11}$$

for indeed the line would differ from $\ell^{(1)}$ only in slope. Setting $y = 0$ and $x = x^{(2)}$ in (1. 11) would then yield

$$x^{(2)} = x^{(1)} - \frac{1}{\tau} \frac{f(x^{(1)})}{f'(x^{(1)})}, \qquad \tau \cdot f'(x^{(1)}) \neq 0, \tag{1.12}$$

and just as the Newton's formula (1. 7) was developed by first considering (1. 5), then from (1. 12) would follow the formula

$$x^{(n+1)} = x^{(n)} - \frac{1}{\tau} \frac{f(x^{(n)})}{f'(x^{(n)})}, \qquad \tau \cdot f'(x^{(n)}) \neq 0. \tag{1.13}$$

If, for simplicity, one sets $w = \frac{1}{\tau}$, then (1. 13) takes the form

$$x^{(n+1)} = x^{(n)} - w \frac{f(x^{(n)})}{f'(x^{(n)})}, \qquad f'(x^{(n)}) \neq 0 \tag{1.14}$$

and is called the <u>generalized Newton's formula.</u> The constant w is called an over-relaxation factor. The iterative method which then uses (1. 14) in place of (1. 7) is called the <u>generalized Newton's method.</u> And, of course, Newton's formula results from (1. 14) in the special case $w = 1$.

<u>Example 3.</u> Approximate the positive root of (1. 8) by the generalized Newton's method.

<u>Solution.</u> The generalized Newton's formula for (1. 8) is

$$x^{(n+1)} = x^{(n)} - w \frac{[x^{(n)}]^3 + \sqrt{3}[x^{(n)}]^2 - 2x^{(n)} - 2\sqrt{3}}{3[x^{(n)}]^2 + 2\sqrt{3}x^{(n)} - 2}. \tag{1.15}$$

Approximating $\sqrt{3}$ by 1.7, setting $x^{(1)} = 2.0$ and $w = 1.3$, and rounding to one decimal place, one has from (1.15) that

$$x^{(2)} \sim 1.4$$

$$x^{(3)} \sim 1.4 \; .$$

Since $x^{(2)} = x^{(3)}$, the iteration will yield no change in the approximation $x \sim 1.4$. Note that this result was obtained with fewer iterations than were required in illustrative Example 1.

Before discussing questions relating to the convergence or divergence of the generalized Newton's method, let us extend the method to systems of equations.

Suppose then that in place of (1.1), which is one equation in one unknown, we have to solve two equations in two unknowns, say

$$f_1(x_1, x_2) = 0 \tag{1.16}$$

$$f_2(x_1, x_2) = 0 \, . \tag{1.17}$$

Then a straightforward extension of (1.14) which we shall use for system (1.16) - (1.17) is

$$x_1^{(n+1)} = x_1^{(n)} - w \frac{f_1(x_1^{(n)}, x_2^{(n)})}{\dfrac{\partial f_1(x_1^{(n)}, x_2^{(n)})}{\partial x_1}} \tag{1.18}$$

$$x_2^{(n+1)} = x_2^{(n)} - w \frac{f_2(x_1^{(n+1)}, x_2^{(n)})}{\dfrac{\partial f_2(x_1^{(n+1)}, x_2^{(n)})}{\partial x_2}} \; . \tag{1.19}$$

Note that formulas (1.18) and (1.19) do not contain matrices, as many other generalizations of Newton's method do, and that the result $x_1^{(n+1)}$, not $x_1^{(n)}$, is used to calculate $x_2^{(n+1)}$.

Example 4. Consider the system of equations

$$e^{x_1} + x_1 - 3x_2 - 3 = 0 \tag{1.20}$$

$$e^{x_2} + x_2 - 2x_1 + 1 = 0 . \tag{1.21}$$

Set

$$f_1(x_1, x_2) = e^{x_1} + x_1 - 3x_2 - 3$$

$$f_2(x_1, x_2) = e^{x_2} + x_2 - 2x_1 + 1 .$$

Then the generalized Newton's formulas (1.18) - (1.19) for system (1.16) - (1.17) take the particular form

$$x_1^{(n+1)} = x_1^{(n)} - w \frac{e^{x_1^{(n)}} + x_1^{(n)} - 3x_2^{(n)} - 3}{e^{x_1^{(n)}} + 1} \tag{1.22}$$

$$x_2^{(n+1)} = x_2^{(n)} - w \frac{e^{x_2^{(n)}} + x_2^{(n)} - 2x_1^{(n+1)} + 1}{e^{x_2^{(n)}} + 1} . \tag{1.23}$$

If one sets $x_1^{(1)} = x_2^{(1)} = 0$ and $w = 1.5$, then (1.22) and (1.23) imply

$$x_1^{(2)} = x_1^{(1)} - 1.5 \frac{(e^{x_1^{(1)}} + x_1^{(1)} - 3x_2^{(1)} - 3)}{e^{x_1^{(1)}} + 1} = 1.5 \tag{1.24}$$

$$x_2^{(2)} = x_2^{(1)} - 1.5\frac{(e^{x_2^{(1)}} + x_2^{(1)} - 2x_1^{(2)} + 1)}{e^{x_2^{(1)}} + 1} = 0.75. \tag{1.25}$$

The results (1.24) and (1.25) would then be inserted into (1.22) and (1.23) to produce $x_1^{(3)}$ and $x_2^{(3)}$, and the iteration would continue in this fashion. The iteration would terminate if and when for some value m one would find that (1.22) and (1.23) yield $x_1^{(m)} = x_1^{(m+1)}$ and $x_2^{(m)} = x_2^{(m+1)}$.

Finally let us extend (1.16) and (1.17) to a system of k equations in k unknowns. Suppose one has to solve a system of equations which has the following form:

$$f_1(x_1, x_2, x_3, \ldots, x_{k-1}, x_k) = 0 \tag{1.26}$$

$$f_2(x_1, x_2, x_3, \ldots, x_{k-1}, x_k) = 0 \tag{1.27}$$

$$f_3(x_1, x_2, x_3, \ldots, x_{k-1}, x_k) = 0 \tag{1.28}$$

$$\vdots$$

$$f_{k-1}(x_1, x_2, x_3, \ldots, x_{k-1}, x_k) = 0 \tag{1.29}$$

$$f_k(x_1, x_2, x_3, \ldots, x_{k-1}, x_k) = 0\ . \tag{1.30}$$

Then the generalized Newton's formulas for system (1.26) - (1.30) which will be of particular value to us are

$$x_1^{(n+1)} = x_1^{(n)} - w\frac{f_1(x_1^{(n)}, x_2^{(n)}, x_3^{(n)}, \ldots, x_{k-1}^{(n)}, x_k^{(n)})}{\dfrac{\partial f_1(x_1^{(n)}, x_2^{(n)}, x_3^{(n)}, \ldots, x_{k-1}^{(n)}, x_k^{(n)})}{\partial x_1}} \tag{1.31}$$

$$(1.32)\qquad x_2^{(n+1)} = x_2^{(n)} - w\frac{f_2(x_1^{(n+1)}, x_2^{(n)}, x_3^{(n)}, \ldots, x_{k-1}^{(n)}, x_k^{(n)})}{\dfrac{\partial f_2(x_1^{(n+1)}, x_2^{(n)}, x_3^{(n)}, \ldots, x_{k-1}^{(n)}, x_k^{(n)})}{\partial x_2}}$$

$$(1.33)\qquad x_3^{(n+1)} = x_3^{(n)} - w\frac{f_3(x_1^{(n+1)}, x_2^{(n+1)}, x_3^{(n)}, \ldots, x_{k-1}^{(n)}, x_k^{(n)})}{\dfrac{\partial f_3(x_1^{(n+1)}, x_2^{(n+1)}, x_3^{(n)}, \ldots, x_{k-1}^{(n)}, x_k^{(n)})}{\partial x_3}}$$

$$\vdots \qquad \vdots \qquad \vdots$$

$$(1.34)\qquad x_{k-1}^{(n+1)} = x_{k-1}^{(n)} - w\frac{f_{k-1}(x_1^{(n+1)}, x_2^{(n+1)}, x_3^{(n+1)}, \ldots, x_{k-2}^{(n+1)}, x_{k-1}^{(n)}, x_k^{(n)})}{\dfrac{\partial f_{k-1}(x_1^{(n+1)}, x_2^{(n+1)}, x_3^{(n+1)}, \ldots, x_{k-2}^{(n+1)}, x_{k-1}^{(n)}, x_k^{(n)})}{\partial x_{k-1}}}$$

$$(1.35)\qquad x_k^{(n+1)} = x_k^{(n)} - w\frac{f_k(x_1^{(n+1)}, x_2^{(n+1)}, \ldots, x_{k-1}^{(n+1)}, x_k^{(n)})}{\dfrac{\partial f_k(x_1^{(n+1)}, x_2^{(n+1)}, \ldots, x_{k-1}^{(n+1)}, x_k^{(n)})}{\partial x_k}} .$$

The application of (1. 31) - (1. 35) to system (1. 26) - (1. 30) will be called the generalized Newton's method for systems.

Without imposing some additional structure on system (1. 26) - (1. 30), it is not possible to prescribe w and $x_1^{(1)}, x_2^{(1)}, \ldots, x_k^{(1)}$ so that the generalized Newton's method will converge to a solution of the system. In the case where system (1. 26) - (1. 30) is linear, the generalized Newton's method is called successive over-relaxation [261, 476], and when such a linear system is derived from elliptic difference equations, as will be done later, it is known [134, 476] that convergence results for all initial vectors and for all w in the range $0 < w < 2$. In certain cases where system (1. 26) - (1. 30) is nonlinear, analogous, though less comprehensive, results are also available [381]. For each such nonlinear system there exist constants a and b in the range $0 \leq a < b \leq 2$ which guarantee the convergence of the generalized Newton's method for all initial vectors provided that $0 \leq a < w < b \leq 2$. It will be interesting to observe, however, that for each system to be considered in these lectures, whether or not it satisfies known sufficiency conditions, we will be able to choose an initial vector and a w so that the generalized Newton's method will solve the system under consideration both quickly and efficiently.

From the computing point of view, the choice of a w and an initial vector which will assure convergence on a computer in a reasonable amount of time is still more of an art than of a science [58, 172, 175, 176, 179, 185, 282], even though nonconstructive results have been obtained for determining an optimal w in the case where (1. 26) - (1. 30) is linear [476]. In practice, one often selects a set of w's in the range $0 < w < 2$, lets each run for, say, ten or fifteen iterations with a zero initial vector, and then chooses that w which seems to be giving the most rapid convergence.

Studies in which the w's in (1. 31) - (1. 35) are allowed to vary have been initiated only recently (see, e. g., [58, 282]).

<u>1. 3. Second Order Partial Differential Equations.</u> On a plane point set the equation

$$(1.37) \quad a\left(x, y, u, \frac{\partial u}{\partial x}, \frac{\partial u}{\partial y}\right)\frac{\partial^2 u}{\partial x^2} + 2b\left(x, y, u, \frac{\partial u}{\partial x}, \frac{\partial u}{\partial y}\right)\frac{\partial^2 u}{\partial x \partial y} + c\left(x, y, u, \frac{\partial u}{\partial x}, \frac{\partial u}{\partial y}\right)\frac{\partial^2 u}{\partial y^2}$$

$$= f\left(x, y, u, \frac{\partial u}{\partial x}, \frac{\partial u}{\partial y}\right),$$

subject to the restriction that at each point in the set

$$(1.38) \qquad a^2 + b^2 + c^2 \neq 0 \,,$$

is said to be a second order partial differential equation. For both practical and theoretical reasons, it is convenient to categorize the various equations of type (1. 37) as follows. At a given point of definition in the plane, equation (1. 37) is said to be

elliptic	if	$b^2 - ac < 0$
parabolic	if	$b^2 - ac = 0$
hyperbolic	if	$b^2 - ac > 0$.

<u>Example 1.</u> At each point in the plane, the equation

$$(1.39) \qquad \frac{\partial^2 u}{\partial x^2} + \frac{\partial^2 u}{\partial y^2} = 0$$

is elliptic. Equation (1. 39) is called the potential, or Laplace's, equation and it is the prototype elliptic partial differential equation.

<u>Example 2.</u> At each point in the plane, the equation

$$(1.40) \qquad \frac{\partial^2 u}{\partial x^2} - \frac{\partial u}{\partial y} = 0$$

is parabolic. Equation (1. 40) is called the heat equation and it is the prototype parabolic partial differential equation.

Example 3. At each point in the plane, the equation

$$\frac{\partial^2 u}{\partial x^2} - \frac{\partial^2 u}{\partial y^2} = 0 \tag{1.41}$$

is hyperbolic. Equation (1. 41) is called the wave equation and it is the prototype hyperbolic partial differential equation.

Example 4. The Tricomi equation

$$y\frac{\partial^2 u}{\partial x^2} + \frac{\partial^2 u}{\partial y^2} = 0 \tag{1.42}$$

is elliptic at each point whose y coordinate is positive, hyperbolic at each point whose y coordinate is negative, and parabolic at each point of the X-axis.

Example 5. The minimal surface equation

$$\left[1+\left(\frac{\partial u}{\partial y}\right)^2\right]\frac{\partial^2 u}{\partial x^2} - 2\frac{\partial u}{\partial x}\frac{\partial u}{\partial y}\frac{\partial^2 u}{\partial x \partial y} + \left[1+\left(\frac{\partial u}{\partial x}\right)^2\right]\frac{\partial^2 u}{\partial y^2} = 0 \tag{1.43}$$

is elliptic at each point of the plane since

$$\begin{aligned} b^2 - ac &= \left(\frac{\partial u}{\partial x}\right)^2\left(\frac{\partial u}{\partial y}\right)^2 - \left[1+\left(\frac{\partial u}{\partial x}\right)^2\right]\left[1+\left(\frac{\partial u}{\partial y}\right)^2\right] \\ &= -1 - \left(\frac{\partial u}{\partial x}\right)^2 - \left(\frac{\partial u}{\partial y}\right)^2 < 0 . \end{aligned}$$

At times it will be convenient to use the notation:

$$u_x = \frac{\partial u}{\partial x}, \quad u_y = \frac{\partial u}{\partial y}, \quad u_{xx} = \frac{\partial^2 u}{\partial x^2}, \quad u_{xy} = \frac{\partial^2 u}{\partial x \partial y}, \quad u_{yy} = \frac{\partial^2 u}{\partial y^2}, \ldots$$

so that, for example, (1.43) can be written in the following equivalent, more compact, form:

$$(1+u_y^2)u_{xx} - 2u_x u_y u_{xy} + (1+u_x^2)u_{yy} = 0 .$$

Note that the character or type of any given second order differential equation is determined completely by the coefficients of the second order derivative terms.

Also, as is usual, note that any function to be considered as a solution of a second order partial differential equation will be assumed to have continuous second order derivatives on the domain of definition of the equation.

1.4. Harmonic Functions and the Dirichlet Problem. Let us begin our study of (1.37) by examining first equations of elliptic type, and indeed let us study first the simplest elliptic differential equation, that is, Laplace's equation (1.39). Alternate ways of writing this equation are

$$u_{xx} + u_{yy} = 0 ,$$

$$\nabla^2 u = 0 ,$$

and

$$\Delta u = 0 .$$

Any function which is a solution of the Laplace equation at each point of the plane is called a harmonic function. If R is a proper subset of the plane and $u(x, y)$ satisfies the Laplace equation at each point of R, then $u(x, y)$ is said to be harmonic on R.

Examples of harmonic functions are $1, 2, -\pi, 10^5, x, -5x, 7y, x^2-y^2$, $x^3-3xy^2, \ldots$. And of fundamental interest and practical value are the following three properties which are possessed by all harmonic functions: Let G be a bounded plane point set whose interior is R is simply connected and whose boundary S is piecewise regular (see Figure 1. 2).

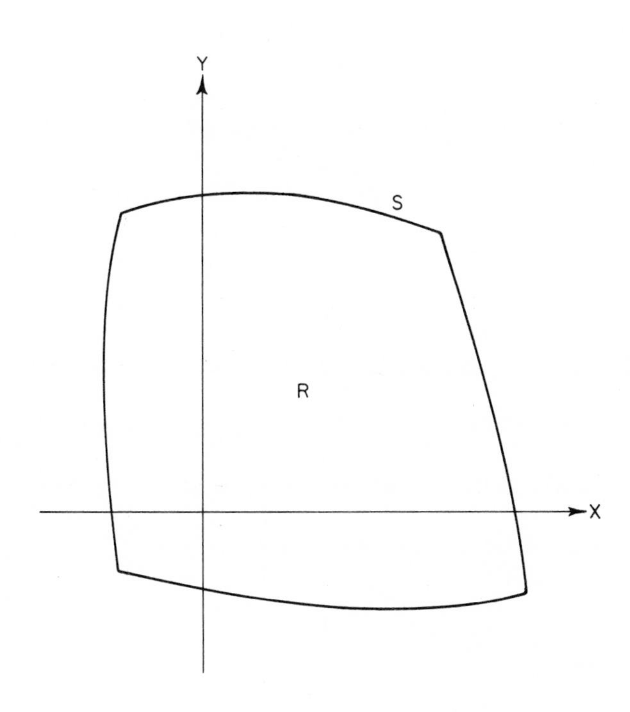

Figure 1.2

If $u(x, y)$ is harmonic on R and continuous on $R+S$, then [74, 165]

Property 1. $u(x, y)$ possesses derivatives of all orders on R.

Property 2. (Strong Max-Min Property). On G, $u(x, y)$ takes on its maximum and minimum values on S.

Property 3. (Mean Value Property). If (x_0, y_0) is a point in R and if

C is any circle in R whose center is (x_0, y_0) and whose radius is r, then

$$u(x_0, y_0) = \frac{1}{2\pi r} \int_C u(x, y) ds, \tag{1.44}$$

where the parameter s represents arc length.

<u>Example</u>. Let S be the rectangle whose sides are parallel to the coordinate axes and whose vertices are (-4, 0), (4, 0), (4, 10), (-4, 10). Let R be the interior of S (consult Figure 1.3). Consider the function

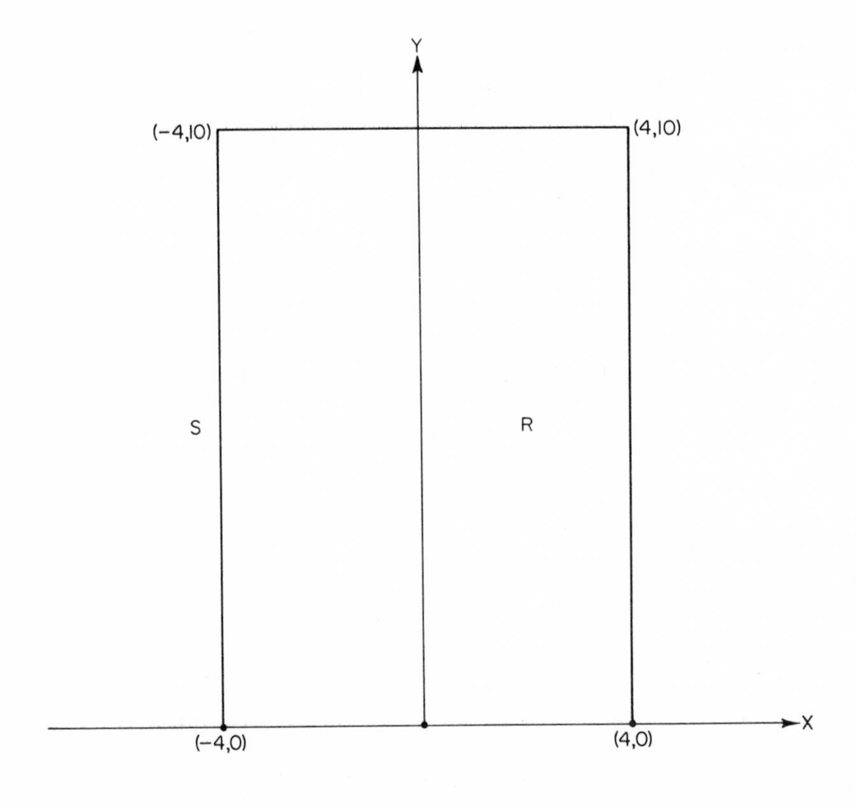

Figure 1.3

$u(x, y) = x^2 - y^2$ on R + S. Then u is continuous on R + S and harmonic on R. By direct calculation

$$u_x = 2x, \quad u_y = -2y, \quad u_{xx} = 2, \quad u_{xy} = 0, \quad u_{yy} = -2$$

and all higher derivatives exist and are equal to zero, which is in accord with Property 1. The maximum value of u on $R + S$ is found by simultaneously maximizing x^2 and minimizing y^2, subject to the constraints $-4 \le x \le 4$, $0 \le y \le 10$. Thus, the maximum value of u is 16 and it is attained at both $(4, 0)$ and $(-4, 0)$, which is in accord with Property 2. The minimum value of u on $R + S$ is found by simultaneously minimizing x^2 and maximizing y^2, subject to the constraints $-4 \le x \le 4$, $0 \le y \le 10$. Thus, the minimum value of u is -100 and it is attained at $(0, 10)$, which is in accord with Property 2. Finally, let C, for example, be the circle of radius 1 with center at $(2, 3)$. Then C can be given parametrically by

$$x = 2 + \sin s, \quad y = 3 + \cos s, \qquad 0 \le s \le 2\pi.$$

Hence

$$\frac{1}{2\pi r} \int_C u\,ds = \frac{1}{2\pi} \int_0^{2\pi} [\,(2 + \sin s)^2 - (3 + \cos s)^2\,]\,ds = -5.$$

However,

$$u(2, 3) = -5,$$

which is in accord with Property 3.

Because there are an infinite number of harmonic functions, we seek next to formulate a set of additional conditions so that any problem involving the Laplace equation and the constraints imposed by these conditions will have one and only one harmonic function for a solution. The simplest such problem is called the interior Dirichlet problem, or more simply, the Dirichlet problem, and it can be stated as follows.

Dirichlet Problem. Let G be a bounded point set whose interior R is simply connected and whose boundary S is piecewise regular. If $f(x, y)$ is given and continuous on S, then the Dirichlet problem for the Laplace equation is that of determining a function $u = u(x, y)$ which is

(a) defined and continuous on $R + S$

(b) harmonic on R, and

(c) identical with $f(x, y)$ on S.

Example. The problem of determining a function $u(x, y)$ such that

(a) u is continuous at each point (x, y) whose coordinates satisfy $x^2 + y^2 \leq 1$;

(b) u is harmonic at each point (x, y) whose coordinates satisfy $x^2 + y^2 < 1$, and

(c) u coincides with $f(x, y) = 1 + x - y$ at each point (x, y) whose coordinates satisfy $x^2 + y^2 = 1$,

is a Dirichlet problem.

The Dirichlet problem is called a boundary value problem because u is prescribed on the boundary S. It can be interpreted geometrically as follows. Since $f(x, y)$ is defined only on S and is continuous on S, the graph of $f(x, y)$ is a closed space curve (see Figure 1. 4). One is being asked in the Dirichlet problem to find a harmonic function whose graph over $R + S$ is a surface which contains the space curve f.

The fact that the Dirichlet problem has a unique solution has been established by a variety of means, including subharmonic and superharmonic functions, finite differences, Green's functions, integral equations,

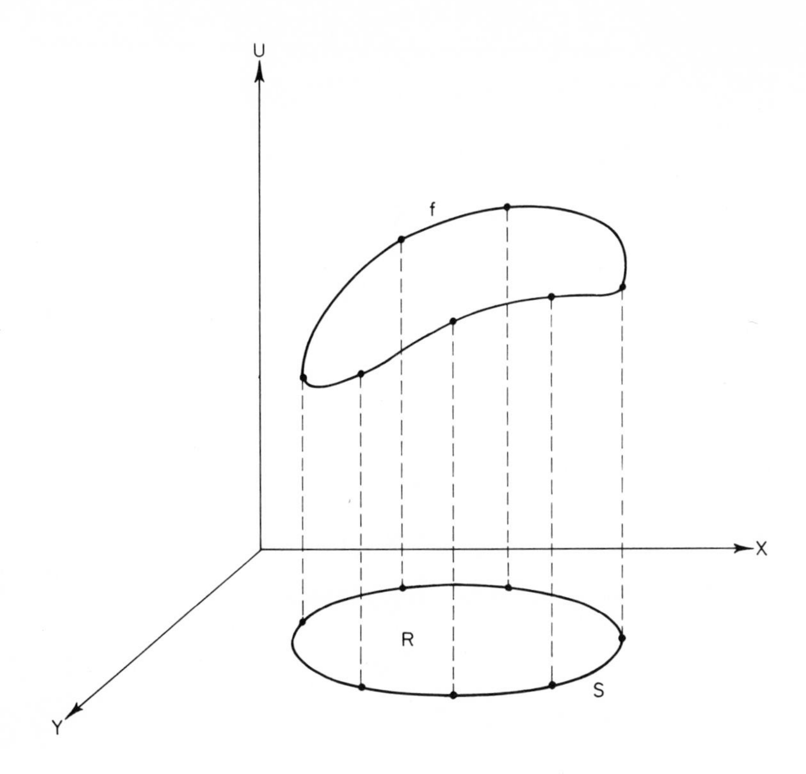

Figure 1.4

Dirichlet's principle and conformal mapping [32, 72, 73, 74, 165, 217, 296, 315, 341, 343, 406] . The analytical determination of $u(x, y)$, however, is a far more difficult problem than that of establishing its existence and uniqueness. If S is a rectangle, then the solution can be given in terms of Fourier series [64, 165, 218] , while if S is a circle or an ellipse then the solution can be given in terms of a Poisson integral or a Fourier series [74, 165, 218, 370] . Also, any problem for which an explicit conformal map can be constructed which takes R onto a rectangular, circular, or elliptic region can be solved in closed form [315] . Beyond these cases, the problems involved in constructing u do not seem to be amenable to existing analytical techniques.

But even in those cases, above, where a solution can be produced as a Fourier series or as an integral, one may not be able to evaluate the solution at a point of interest because the series may be slowly convergent or because the integrand may not have an antiderivative.

Because it is known that the Dirichlet problem always has a unique solution, because in most problems the solutions cannot be given in closed form, and because in those few problems having closed form solutions these solutions can rarely be evaluated at a particular point of interest, we shall seek in the next lecture to approximate the solution of the Dirichlet problem by means of a high speed, digital computer technique. For the present, we conclude by discussing other kinds of problems which are of interest with regard to the Laplace equation.

If in the statement of the Dirichlet problem, one were to replace the boundary values $u = f(x, y)$ on S by normal derivative values $\frac{\partial u}{\partial n} = g(x, y)$, then the resulting problem is called a Neumann problem, and such problems, in general, have an infinite number of solutions, any two of which differ only by an additive constant [74, 343]. If in the statement of the Dirichlet problem one prescribes function values $u = f(x, y)$ on a nonempty, proper subset of S and normal derivatives $\frac{\partial u}{\partial n} = g(x, y)$ on the remainder of S, then the resulting problem is called a Mixed Type problem and it, in general, has a unique solution [74, 343]. A final type of problem associated with the Laplace equation which is intimately associated with the propagation of outgoing waves is the exterior Dirichlet problem, and it is formulated as follows:

<u>Exterior Dirichlet Problem.</u> Let G be a bounded point set whose interior R is simply connected and whose boundary S is piecewise regular. Let R^* be the exterior of G. If $f(x, y)$ is given and continuous on S, then the exterior Dirichlet problem for the Laplace equation is that of determining a function $u(x, y)$ on $R^* + S$ which is

(a) defined and continuous on $R^* + S$

(b) harmonic on R^*

(c) identical with $f(x, y)$ on S, and

(d) bounded on $R^* + S$.

It is known that the exterior Dirichlet problem has a unique solution [74, 343], but in general no analytical technique is available at present for the construction of the solution.

Lecture 2 - Numerical Solution of the Interior and the Exterior Dirichlet Problems.

2.1. Introduction. With the knowledge that high speed digital computers can perform arithmetic operations with exceptional speed, we will attempt to approximate solutions of differential equations problems by first approximating these problems by algebraic problems, and then by solving the latter on a computer. In the process, all continuous data and equations will be discretized, so that infinite point sets will be approximated by finite point sets and differential equations will be approximated by difference equations.

2.2. A Difference Equation Approximation of the Laplace Equation. Let the points (x, y), $(x+h_1, y)$, $(x, y+h_2)$, $(x-h_3, y)$, $(x, y-h_4)$, where h_1, h_2, h_3, h_4 and h are positive constants which satisfy

$$0 < h_i \le h, \qquad i = 1, 2, 3, 4, \tag{2.1}$$

be numbered $0, 1, 2, 3, 4$, respectively, as shown in Figure 2.1. Let $u(x, y)$ at a point numbered i be denoted for simplicity by u_i, and let us try to determine parameters $\alpha_0, \alpha_1, \alpha_2, \alpha_3, \alpha_4$ such that at (x, y)

$$u_{xx} + u_{yy} \equiv \sum_0^4 \alpha_i u_i . \tag{2.2}$$

Since there are five parameters α_i, we seek five relations from which to determine them. Substitution into (2.2) of Taylor expansions about (x, y)

or u_1, u_2, u_3, u_4 and regrouping terms implies

$$(2.3)\qquad u_{xx} + u_{yy} \equiv u_0(\alpha_0 + \alpha_1 + \alpha_2 + \alpha_3 + \alpha_4) + u_x(h_1\alpha_1 - h_3\alpha_3) + u_y(h_2\alpha_2 - h_4\alpha_4) + \frac{u_{xx}}{2}(h_1^2\alpha_1 + h_3^2\alpha_3) + \frac{u_{yy}}{2}(h_2^2\alpha_2 + h_4^2\alpha_4) + \sum_1^4 [O(\alpha_i h_i^3)] .$$

If (2.3) were to be valid for all functions u, then the corresponding coefficients of u_0, u_x, u_y, u_{xx} and u_{yy} would be equal. Thus

$$(2.4)\qquad \begin{cases} \alpha_0 + \alpha_1 + \alpha_2 + \alpha_3 + \alpha_4 = 0 \\ h_1\alpha_1 - h_3\alpha_3 = 0 \\ h_2\alpha_2 - h_4\alpha_4 = 0 \\ h_1^2\alpha_1 + h_3^2\alpha_3 = 2 \\ h_2^2\alpha_2 + h_4^2\alpha_4 = 2 , \end{cases}$$

the unique solution of which is

$$(2.5)\qquad \alpha_0 = -2\left[\frac{1}{h_1h_3} + \frac{1}{h_2h_4}\right], \quad \alpha_1 = \frac{2}{h_1(h_1+h_3)}, \quad \alpha_2 = \frac{2}{h_2(h_2+h_4)}, \quad \alpha_3 = \frac{2}{h_3(h_1+h_3)}, \quad \alpha_4 = \frac{2}{h_4(h_2+h_4)} .$$

Substitution of (2.5) into (2.2) implies then that at (x, y)

$$(2.6)\qquad u_{xx}+u_{yy} \equiv -2\left[\frac{1}{h_1h_3} + \frac{1}{h_2h_4}\right]u_0 + \frac{2}{h_1(h_1+h_3)}u_1 + \frac{2}{h_2(h_2+h_4)}u_2 + \frac{2}{h_3(h_1+h_3)}u_3 + \frac{2}{h_4(h_2+h_4)}u_4 + \sum_{i=1}^4 [O(h_i)] .$$

Hence, elimination of the terms $\sum_{i=1}^{4} [O(h_i)]$ in (2. 6) implies that a difference equation approximation of the Laplace equation is

(2. 7)
$$-\left[\frac{2}{h_1h_3}+\frac{2}{h_2h_4}\right]u_0+\frac{2}{h_1(h_1+h_3)}u_1+\frac{2}{h_2(h_2+h_4)}u_2$$
$$+\frac{2}{h_3(h_1+h_3)}u_3+\frac{2}{h_4(h_2+h_4)}u_4=0\ .$$

Note that in the particular case where $h_1 = h_2 = h_3 = h_4$, then (2. 7) implies

(2. 8)
$$u_0=\frac{u_1+u_2+u_3+u_4}{4}$$

which says that u_0 is the mean value of u_1, u_2, u_3 and u_4. Relationship (2. 8) is the discrete analogue of the mean value property for harmonic functions. Note also that the numbering 0, 1, 2, 3, 4 is not essential to the form of (2. 7). Thus, if 0, 1, 2, 3, 4 were replaced respectively by 11, 5, 3, 6, 9, then (2. 7) need be altered only be replacing u_0, u_1, u_2, u_3, u_4 by $u_{11}, u_5, u_3, u_6, u_9$, respectively.

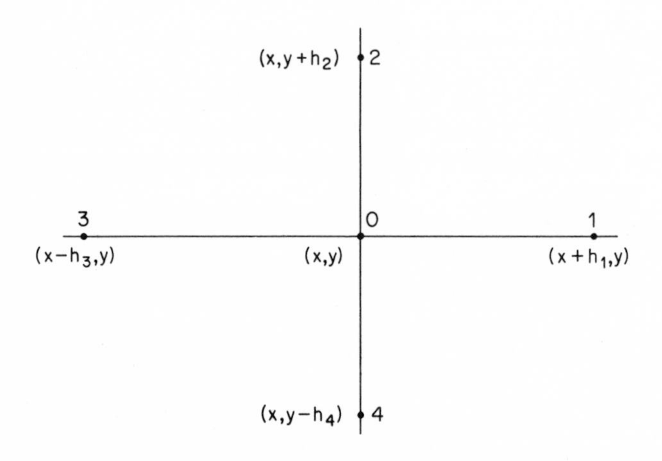

Figure 2.1

2.3. Interior and Boundary Lattice Points. Consider now discretizing the point set $G = R + S$ given in the statement of the Dirichlet problem. Let $(\bar{x}, \bar{y})$ be an arbitrary, but fixed, point in the plane and let h be a positive constant called the grid size. The set of points $(\bar{x} + ph, \bar{y} + qh)$; $p = 0, \pm 1, \pm 2, \ldots$; $q = 0, \pm 1, \pm 2, \ldots$, is called a set of planar grid points. The set of vertical lines $x = \bar{x} + ph$, $p = 0, \pm 1, \pm 2, \ldots$, and of horizontal lines $y = \bar{y} + qh$, $q = 0, \pm 1, \pm 2, \ldots$, is called a planar lattice. Those planar grid points which are also points of R are called interior lattice (or grid) points and are denoted by R_h.

Let the set of points which S and the planar lattice have in common be denoted by S_h^* and set $G_h^* = R_h + S_h^*$. The four neighbors of a point (x, y) in R_h are defined to be those four points in G_h^* which are closest to (x, y) in the east, north, west, and south directions. Let G_h be that subset of G_h^* which consists of each point of R_h and its four neighbors. Then, finally, the boundary lattice (or grid) points, denoted by S_h, are defined by $S_h = G_h - R_h$.

Example. Let R be the bounded region whose boundary S is the triangle with vertices $(0,0)$, $(7,0)$, $(0,7)$. Set $(\bar{x}, \bar{y}) = (0,0)$ and $h = 2$ (consult Figure 2.2). Let L_1 be the side of S which joins $(0,7)$ and $(0,0)$, let L_2 be the side joining $(0,0)$ and $(7,0)$, and let L_3 be the side joining $(7,0)$ and $(0,7)$. Then the points of R_h are $(2,2)$, $(2,4)$ and $(4,2)$ and have been crossed in Figure 2.2. The points S_h^* are all of the points in L_1 and L_2 and the four circled and two squared points of L_3 shown in the figure. The points of S_h are (2, 0), (4, 0), (0, 2), (5, 2), (4, 3), (0, 4), (3, 4), and (2, 5), which are circled in Figure 2. 2.

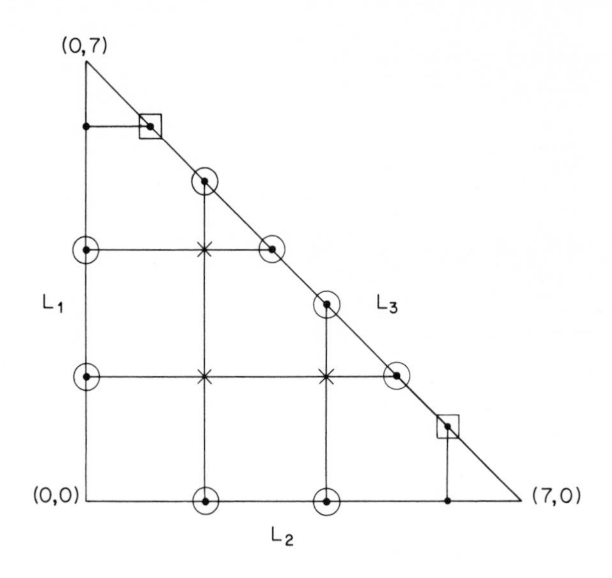

Figure 2.2

2. 4. The Numerical Method. The following numerical method will now be presented for approximating the solution of the Dirichlet problem.

Method D. For fixed $h > 0$ and fixed $(\bar{x}, \bar{y})$, construct R_h and S_h. Suppose R_h consists of m points and S_h consists of n points. Number the points in R_h in a one-to-one fashion with the integers 1-m in such a way that the numbers are increasing from left to right on any horizontal line of the lattice and increasing from bottom to top on any vertical line of the lattice. Number the points of S_h in a one-to-one fashion with the integers $m+1, m+2, \ldots, m+n$. Then:

Step 1. At each point of S_h, set $U(x, y) = f(x, y)$. If (x, y) is numbered k, hen in subscript notation, this is equivalent to $U_k = f(x, y)$.

Step 2. At each point (x, y) of R_h, beginning with the one numbered 1 and continuing in consecutive order through the one numbered m, write down the Laplace difference analogue in the form

$$
(2.9)\quad -\left(\frac{2}{h_1 h_3} + \frac{2}{h_2 h_4}\right) U(x,y) + \frac{2}{h_1(h_1+h_3)} U(x+h_1, y) + \frac{2}{h_2(h_2+h_4)} U(x, y+h_2) + \frac{2}{h_3(h_1+h_3)} U(x-h_3, y) + \frac{2}{h_4(h_2+h_4)} U(x, y-h_4) = 0,
$$

where $(x+h_1, y)$, $(x, y+h_2)$, $(x-h_3, y)$, $(x, y-h_4)$ are the neighbors of (x, y). If in applying (2.9) at a point (x, y), any of the neighbors $(x+h_1, y)$, $(x, y+h_2)$, $(x-h_3, y)$, $(x, y-h_4)$ are points of S_h, then in (2.9) replace U at these points by the known values f determined in Step 1. In practice each equation should be written in subscript notation, as demonstrated in (2.7). These results, then, a linear algebraic system of m equations in the m unknowns $U_1, U_2, \ldots, U_m$.

Step 3. Solve the algebraic system generated in Step 2.

Step 4. Let the function U_i, $i = 1, 2, \ldots, m+n$, which is defined only on $R_h + S_h$ represent on $R_h + S_h$ the approximate solution of the given Dirichlet problem.

Example. Let S be the triangle with vertices $(0, 0)$, $(7, 0)$, $(0, 7)$ and let R be the interior of S. On $R + S$ consider the Dirichlet problem with $f(x, y) = x^2 - y^2$. Set $(\bar{x}, \bar{y}) = (0, 0)$ and $h = 2$, as in the example in

Section 2. 3. As shown in Figure 2. 3, the points of R_h are numbered 1-3

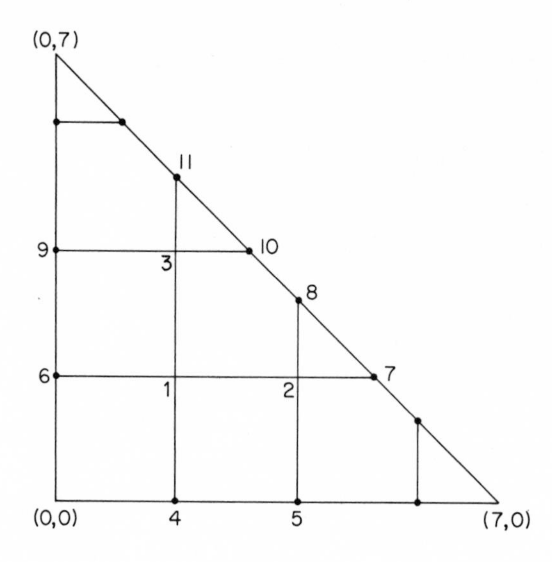

Figure 2.3

while those of S_h are numbered 4-18. Following the directions of Step 1, one has

$$U_4 = 4, \quad U_5 = 16, \quad U_6 = -4$$

(2.10) $$U_7 = 21, \quad U_8 = 7, \quad U_9 = -16,$$

$$U_{10} = -7, \quad U_{11} = -21.$$

Application of (2. 9) at the point numbered 1 in Figure 2. 3 and substitution from (2. 10) yields

$$(-1)U_1 + \frac{1}{4}U_2 + \frac{1}{4}U_3 + \frac{1}{4}(-4) + \frac{1}{4}(4) = 0$$

or

(2. 11) $$-U_1 + \frac{1}{4}U_2 + \frac{1}{4}U_3 = 0 .$$

pplication of (2. 9) at the point numbered 2 in Figure 2. 3 and substitution
om (2. 10) yields

$$-2U_2 + \frac{2}{1(1+2)}(21) + \frac{2}{1(1+2)}(7) + \frac{2}{2(1+2)}U_1 + \frac{2}{2(1+2)}(16) = 0,$$

r

(2. 12) $$\frac{1}{3}U_1 - 2U_2 = -24.$$

pplication of (2. 9) at the point numbered 3 in Figure 2. 3 and substitution
om (2. 10) yields

$$-2U_3 + \frac{2}{1(1+2)}(-7) + \frac{2}{1(1+2)}(-21) + \frac{2}{2(1+2)}(-16) + \frac{2}{2(1+2)}U_1 = 0,$$

r

(2. 13) $$\frac{1}{3}U_1 - 2U_3 = 24 .$$

he solution of (2. 11) - (2. 13) is

(2. 14) $$U_1 = 0, \quad U_2 = 12, \quad U_3 = -12.$$

hus, U_i, $i = 1, 2, \ldots, 11$, as given by (2. 10) and (2. 14) constitutes the
pproximate solution to the given Dirichlet problem on $R_h + S_h$.

Observe that Method D prescribes an ordering to the system of
lgebraic equations generated in Step 3, that is, there is a first equation,
second equation, ..., an mth equation. The significance of the ordering
s that in the ith equation, $i = 1, 2, \ldots, m$, the coefficient of x_i is, in
bsolute value, the maximum coefficient in the equation, a property which
s very useful when discussing the iterative solution of large linear
lgebraic systems by iteration.

The reasonableness of Method D as a numerical method follows from the facts that

(a) the approximate solution always exists and is unique [171],

(b) that for a large class of problems the numerical solution converges to the analytical solution as $h \to 0$ [171], and

(c) the system of algebraic equations generated by Method D can be solved by the generalized Newton's method which converges for any initial guess and any w in the range $0 < w < 2$ [134, 428, 476].

In actual practice, it is a simple matter in applying Method D to allow R_h to have 25,000 points and to solve the resulting system on the CDC 3600 by the generalized Newton's method in about 25 minutes.

2.5. Numerical Solution of the Exterior Dirichlet Problem. The exterior Dirichlet problem can also be solved very easily numerically by means of Method D if one first transforms it into an equivalent Dirichlet problem. This can be done in the following fashion.

Let C be a circle whose center is $(0,0)$ and whose radius is r (> 0). Let L be any half line whose initial point is the origin (consult Figure 2.4). If $P(x,y)$ is any point on L which is different from the origin, then the unique point $Q(\xi, \eta)$ on L for which

$$|0P| \cdot |0Q| = r^2 \tag{2.15}$$

is called the inverse point of P with regard to C. The mapping of all points of the plane, other than the origin, into their inverse points is called an inversion mapping. In effect, points inside C map into points

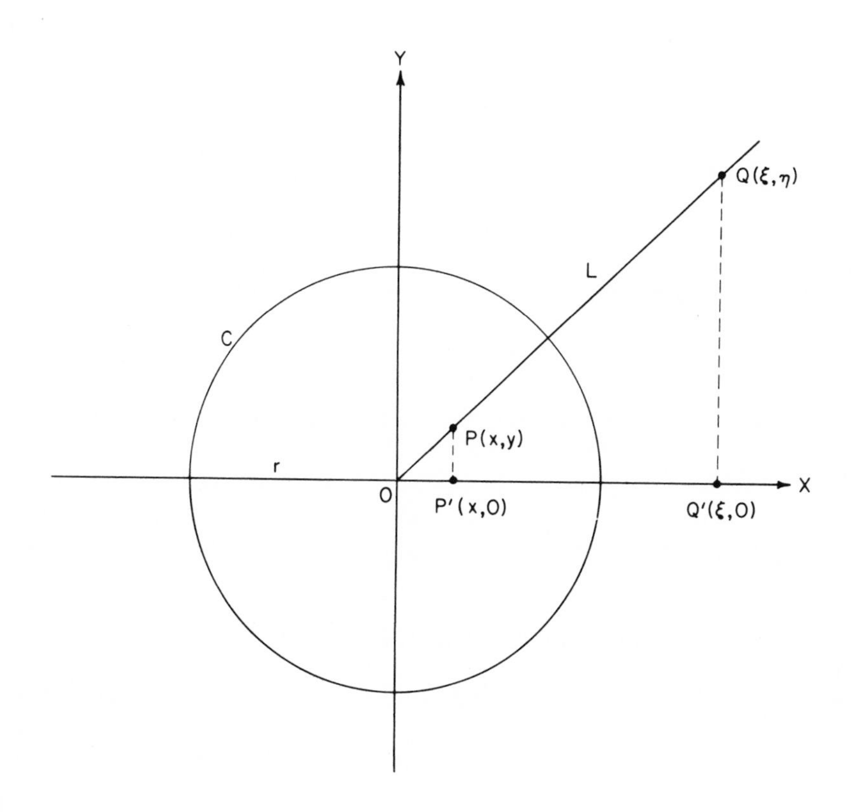

Figure 2.4

outside C, points on C map into themselves, and all points outside C map into points inside C. This last observation that all points outside C map into points inside C, which in effect maps an unbounded set of points into a bounded one, will be of particular value to us. First, however, let us develop the equations of an inversion mapping.

In Figure 2. 4, let the foot of the perpendicular to the X-axis through P be P' and that of the perpendicular through Q be Q'. Then, by similar triangles,

(2.16) $$\frac{x}{\sqrt{x^2+y^2}} = \frac{\xi}{\sqrt{\xi^2+\eta^2}} .$$

From (2.15), however,

(2.17) $$\sqrt{x^2+y^2} \cdot \sqrt{\xi^2+\eta^2} = r^2$$

so that (2.16) can be rewritten in the form

(2.18) $$\xi = \frac{xr^2}{x^2+y^2}, \qquad x^2 + y^2 \neq 0 .$$

Similarly, by dropping perpendiculars to the y axis, it follows that

(2.19) $$\eta = \frac{yr^2}{x^2+y^2}, \qquad x^2 + y^2 \neq 0 .$$

Formulas (2.18) and (2.19) are convenient for determining ξ and η when x and y are given. For transforming a given equation in x and y to one in ξ and η, it is more convenient to have (2.18) and (2.19) solved for x and y in terms of ξ and η. By means of (2.17), these formulas can be written in the form

(2.20) $$x = \frac{\xi r^2}{\xi^2+\eta^2}, \qquad \xi^2 + \eta^2 \neq 0$$

(2.21) $$y = \frac{\eta r^2}{\xi^2+\eta^2}, \qquad \xi^2 + \eta^2 \neq 0 .$$

In the particular case when $r = 1$, formulas (2.18) - (2.21) reduce to

(2.22) $$\xi = \frac{x}{x^2+y^2}, \quad \eta = \frac{y}{x^2+y^2}, \qquad x^2 + y^2 \neq 0$$

(2.23) $$x = \frac{\xi}{\xi^2+\eta^2}, \quad y = \frac{\eta}{\xi^2+\eta^2}, \qquad \xi^2 + \eta^2 \neq 0 .$$

Example. Under inversion with respect to the unit circle, find the coordinates of the points into which $(\frac{1}{2}, 0)$ and $(-3, 4)$ are mapped.

Solution. From (2.22), one has first

$$\xi = \frac{\frac{1}{2}}{(\frac{1}{2})^2 + 0^2} = 2, \qquad \eta = \frac{0}{(\frac{1}{2})^2 + 0^2} = 0,$$

so that $(\frac{1}{2}, 0)$ is mapped into $(2, 0)$. Similarly $(-3, 4)$ is mapped into $(-\frac{3}{25}, \frac{4}{25})$.

Consider now the following well known theorem.

Theorem 2.1. Let $u(x, y)$ be the solution of the exterior Dirichlet problem. Without loss of generality [165], assume that $(0, 0)$ is in R. Under inversion with respect to, say, the unit circle let

$$R^* \rightarrow R^i,$$

$$S \rightarrow S^i,$$

(2.24) $$u(x, y) = u(\frac{\xi}{\xi^2+\eta^2}, \frac{\eta}{\xi^2+\eta^2}) = v(\xi, \eta),$$

(2.25) $$f(x, y) = f(\frac{\xi}{\xi^2+\eta^2}, \frac{\eta}{\xi^2+\eta^2}) = F(\xi, \eta).$$

Then $v(\xi, \eta)$ is the solution of the Dirichlet problem on $R^i + S^i$ with boundary values F, that is

(a) $$\frac{\partial^2 v}{\partial \xi^2} + \frac{\partial^2 v}{\partial \eta^2} = 0, \qquad (\xi, \eta) \text{ in } R^i,$$

(b) $v(\xi, \eta)$ is defined and continuous on $R^i + S^i$, and

(c) $$v(\xi, \eta) = F(\xi, \eta) \quad \text{on } S^i.$$

For a proof of Theorem 2.1, see, for example, [342]. The impact of the theorem is that it allows us to solve numerically by Method D a Dirichlet problem for v and then to determine approximate values for u by means of (2.24).

<u>Example</u>. Let S be the unit square with vertices $(\frac{1}{2},\frac{1}{2})$, $(-\frac{1}{2},\frac{1}{2})$, $(-\frac{1}{2},-\frac{1}{2})$, $(\frac{1}{2},-\frac{1}{2})$ and let R^* be the exterior of S. Let

$$f(x,y) = \frac{x^2-y^2}{(x^2+y^2)^2}, \quad (x,y) \text{ on } S. \tag{2.26}$$

Consider then the resulting exterior Dirichlet problem, which is shown diagramatically in Figure 2.5. Now, under inversion with respect to the

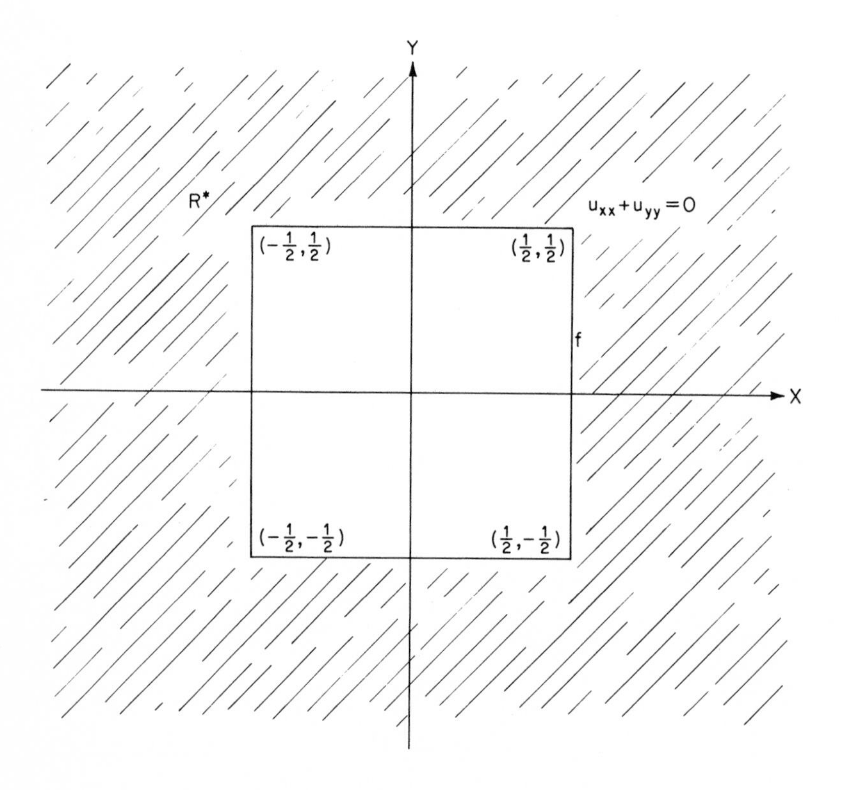

Figure 2.5

unit circle, the four points $(\frac{1}{2}, \frac{1}{2})$, $(\frac{1}{2}, -\frac{1}{2})$, $(-\frac{1}{2}, \frac{1}{2})$, $(-\frac{1}{2}, -\frac{1}{2})$ map into $(1, 1)$, $(1, -1)$, $(-1, 1)$, $(-1, -1)$, respectively, in the ξ-η plane, as shown in Figure 2. 6. The sides of the given unit square map into the four semicircles shown in Figure 2. 6, since, for example, the equation

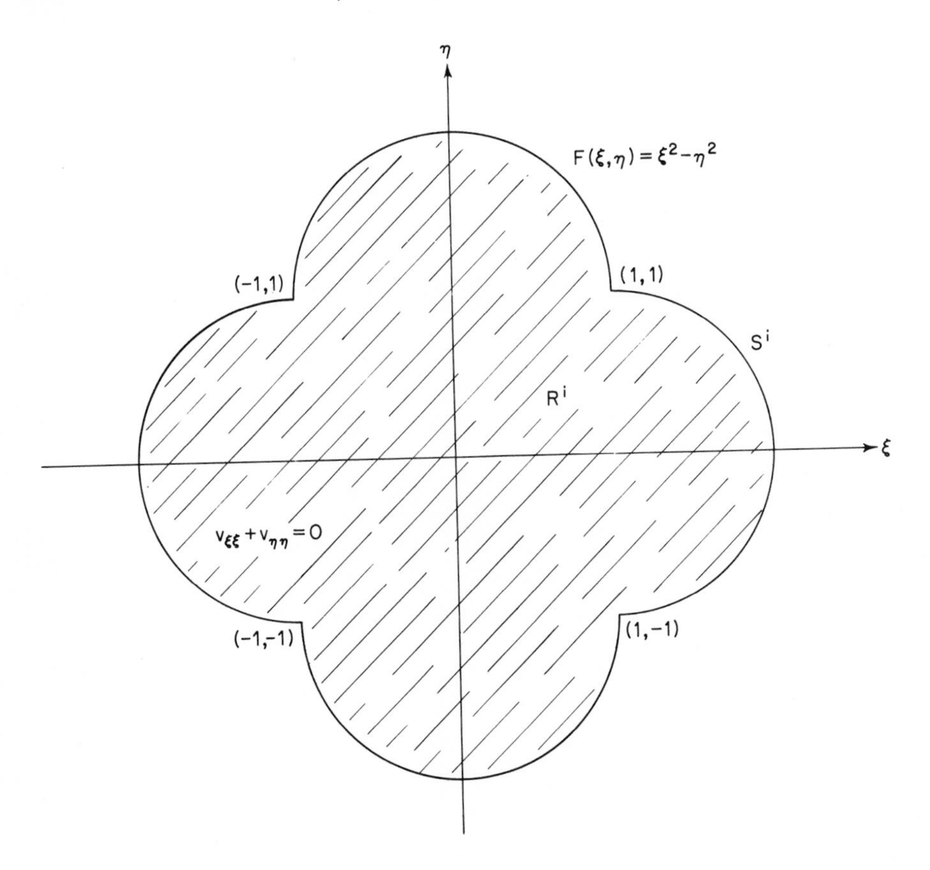

Figure 2.6

(2. 27) $$x = \frac{1}{2}$$

maps, by (2. 23) into

$$\frac{\xi}{\xi^2 + \eta^2} = \frac{1}{2} ,$$

or, equivalently, into

(2.28) $$(\xi-1)^2 + \eta^2 = 1.$$

In the X-Y plane, the side of the square joining $(\frac{1}{2}, \frac{1}{2})$ and $(-\frac{1}{2}, \frac{1}{2})$ is only a portion of the straight line whose equation is (2.27), while in the ξ-η plane, the map of this segment is the semicircle joining (1, 1) and (-1, 1), which is the corresponding portion of the circle whose equation is (2.28). The unbounded region R^* in the X-Y plane maps into the bounded region R^i in the ξ-η plane and

(2.29) $$f(x, y) = \frac{x^2 - y^2}{(x^2+y^2)^2} = \xi^2 - \eta^2 = F(\xi, \eta) .$$

For the resulting Dirichlet problem defined on $R^i + S^i$, and shown geometrically in Figure 2.6, Method D was applied with $(\bar{\xi}, \bar{\eta}) = (0, 0)$ and $h = 0.02$. The resulting 25,649 linear equations in as many unknowns was reduced by symmetry to 6512 equations in as many unknowns. These were solved by the generalized Newton's method on the CDC 3600 with a zero initial guess and with $w = 1.94$. The number of iterations was 287 and the running time was 4 minutes and 49 seconds. The results were known to be correct to at least six decimal places because in this problem the exact solution, namely $v(\xi, \eta) = \xi^2 - \eta^2$, was known. Some typical results are recorded in Table 1.

Table 1

ξ	η	x	y	Computed Value	Exact Value $u(x, y) = v(\xi, \eta)$
0.0000	0.0200	0.0000	50.0000	0.00040005	0.00040000
0.0400	0.7600	0.0691	1.3122	-0.57600067	-0.57600000
0.1400	0.1800	2.6923	3.4615	-0.01280012	-0.01280000
0.2600	1.5800	0.1014	0.6162	-2.42880003	-2.42880000
0.4200	0.3400	1.4384	1.1644	0.06080005	0.06080000
0.5000	0.0200	1.9968	0.0799	0.24960062	0.24960000
0.6400	0.2600	1.3412	0.5448	0.34200036	0.34200000
1.1800	0.3000	0.7960	0.2024	1.30240017	1.30240000

2.6. Observation. It should be noted that Method D extends easily to mixed type problems [24, 49, 50, 167, 171, 251, 420, 438, 442], but in general, with less accuracy. Rather than introduce these ideas now, we shall do so in a natural way when considering problems for which such conditions are important, and will show at that time how to deal with them. We will not attempt to deal with pure Neumann problems because they are not well posed. Note however that prescribing the solution of a Neumann problem at only one boundary point transforms the problem to a mixed type problem.

Lecture 3 - Numerical Solution of Problems for General Linear and Singular Elliptic Equations

3.1. Introduction. In this lecture we will consider those modifications of Method D which are necessary when the Laplace equation is replaced by some other linear elliptic differential equation. The discussion will focus on equations which occur repeatedly in physical applications.

3.2. The General Linear Elliptic Differential Equation with Constant Coefficients. If A, B and C are constants, it is known [165] that the partial differential equation

$$Au_{xx} + 2Bu_{xy} + Cu_{yy} + Du_x + Eu_y + Fu + G(x,y) = 0, \quad A^2+B^2+C^2 \neq 0 \tag{3.1}$$

can be simplified by a rotation of axes. If (3.1) is elliptic, one can thereby eliminate the u_{xy} term so that, without loss of generality, we can, and do, consider (3.1) in the form

$$Au_{xx} + Cu_{yy} + Du_x + Eu_y + Fu + G(x,y) = 0 \tag{3.2}$$

where A, C, D, E and F are constants, where

$$A > 0, \quad C > 0, \tag{3.3}$$

and where $G(x,y)$ is continuous. Further, for theoretical purposes it will be convenient to know that any solution of (3.2) has certain properties in common with harmonic functions, and this will be assured [74] by the further assumption that

$$F \leq 0. \tag{3.4}$$

To construct a difference analogue of (3. 2), consider the same five point arrangement shown in Figure 2. 1 and at (x, y) set

$$(3.5)\qquad Au_{xx} + Cu_{yy} + Du_x + Eu_y + Fu + G(x,y) \equiv \sum_{i=0}^{4} \alpha_i u_i + G(x,y).$$

Substitution of finite Taylor expansions about (x, y) into (3. 5) and setting corresponding coefficients equal, as in (2. 4), implies

$$\begin{aligned}
\alpha_0 + \alpha_1 + \alpha_2 + \alpha_3 + \alpha_4 &= F\\
h_1\alpha_1 - h_3\alpha_3 &= D\\
h_2\alpha_2 - h_4\alpha_4 &= E\\
h_1^2\alpha_1 + h_3^2\alpha_3 &= 2A\\
h_2^2\alpha_2 + h_4^2\alpha_4 &= 2C,
\end{aligned}$$

the solution of which is

$$\alpha_0 = \frac{Fh_1h_2h_3h_4 - 2Ah_2h_4 - 2Ch_1h_3 - Dh_2h_4(h_3-h_1) - Eh_1h_3(h_2-h_4)}{h_1h_2h_3h_4}$$

$$(3.6)\qquad \alpha_1 = \frac{2A + Dh_3}{h_1(h_1+h_3)}, \qquad \alpha_2 = \frac{2C + Eh_4}{h_2(h_2+h_4)}$$

$$\alpha_3 = \frac{2A - Dh_1}{h_3(h_1+h_3)}, \qquad \alpha_4 = \frac{2C - Eh_2}{h_4(h_2+h_4)}$$

Thus, a difference equation analogue of (3. 2) is

$$(3.7)\qquad \sum_{i=0}^{4} \alpha_i u_i + G(x,y) = 0,$$

where the α_i are given by (3. 6).

If one is given a Dirichlet problem in which the Laplace equation is replaced by (3. 2), then Method D need be modified only by replacing (2. 9) with

(3. 8) $$\sum_{i=0}^{4} \alpha_i U_i + G(x, y) = 0 .$$

However, if one wishes to be assured, a priori, that the theoretical results available for Method D are also valid for the modified method, then [171] one need only select h small enough so that in (3. 6) one has

(3. 9) $$\alpha_0 < 0; \ \alpha_i > 0, \quad i = 1, 2, 3, 4.$$

This additional condition can be satisfied easily by choosing

(3. 10) $$\max \left[\frac{h|D|}{2A}, \frac{h|E|}{2C} \right] < 1.$$

Note that elliptic equations which do not satisfy (3. 4) may have solutions which do not possess any form of a max-min property [74]. Such equations arise naturally by applying the process of separation of variables to various hyperbolic partial differential equations. Because they require a radically different approach than that being developed, they will not be discussed in these lectures (see, however, [184]).

3. 3. Singular Problems. In the broad spectrum of scientific and technological research, one encounters the interesting equations shown in Table 3. 1. Moreover, the problems of physical interest for all the equations in Table 3. 1 are defined on a region R whose boundary S includes a nondegenerate portion of the X-axis (see Figure 3. 1), and on such regions the coefficient of the u_y term in each equation becomes infinite as $y \rightarrow 0$.

Table 3.1

Equation	Field of Study
1. $u_{xx} + u_{yy} + \frac{1}{y}u_y = 0$	1. Potential of electric, magnetic and gravitational fields; steady flow of heat, electric current and ideal fluids.
2. $u_{xx} + u_{yy} - \frac{1}{y}u_y = 0$	2. Streamlines of steady fluid flow.
3. $u_{xx} + u_{yy} + \frac{3}{y}u_y = 0$	3. Torsion of a shaft.
4. $u_{xx} + u_{yy} - \frac{3}{y}u_y = 0$	4. Stress concentration theory
5. $u_{xx} + u_{yy} + \frac{5}{y}u_y = 0$	5. Stress concentration theory.

Because each equation in Table 3.1 is linear elliptic on such regions, and because each has an unbounded coefficient as $y \to 0$, the equations are said to be singular on R and the resulting class of boundary value problems will be called singular problems.

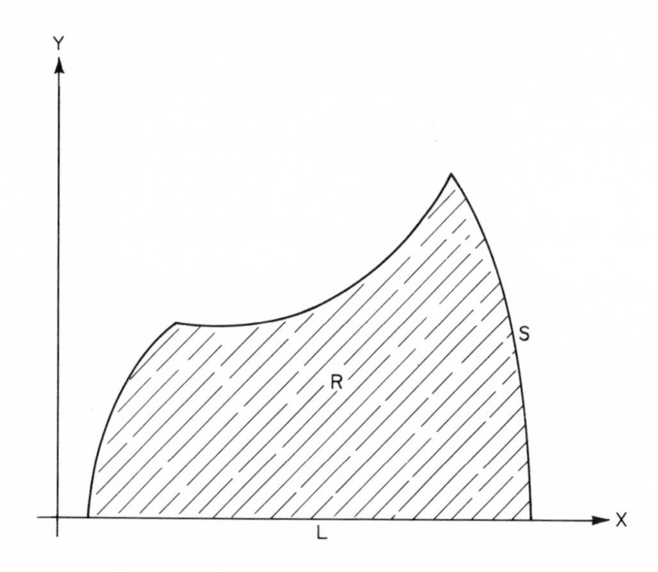

Figure 3.1

Now in any analytical approach to such singular problems, it is very likely that a mathematician would note that each equation in Table 3.1 is of the form

$$(3.11) \qquad u_{xx} + u_{yy} + \frac{K}{y} u_y = 0, \quad K \text{ a nonzero constant,}$$

and would therefore consider the Dirichlet problem for (3.11) on $R + S$. Such an approach would be completely comprehensive and avoid much duplication. Surprisingly enough, recent results indicate that such an effort would be futile. These results are incorporated in the following theorem.

Theorem 3.1. Let R be a simply connected, bounded region whose boundary S is piecewise regular. Let L be a subset of S which is also a nondegenerate interval on the X-axis. Then

(a) if $f(x, y)$ is defined and continuous on S and if $K < 1$ then the associated Dirichlet problem for (3.11) has a unique solution [379];

(b) if $f(x, y)$ is defined, continuous and bounded on $S-L$ and if $K \geq 1$, then the associated Dirichlet problem for (3.11) has a unique solution [206].

The important implication of Theorem 3.1 is that for $K \geq 1$, one must not prescribe $f(x, y)$ on L if one is to expect the resulting Dirichlet problem to have a solution, that is, if $K \geq 1$ and if $f(x, y)$ is prescribed only on $S-L$, then indeed u is completely determined on L. For the case $K < 1$, $f(x, y)$ can be prescribed in the usual way on S and the resulting Dirichlet problem is well posed.

Example. Let S be the unit square with vertices $(0, 0)$, $(1, 0)$, $(1, 1)$ and

(0, 1), as shown in Figure 3. 2, and let R be the interior of S. Let the

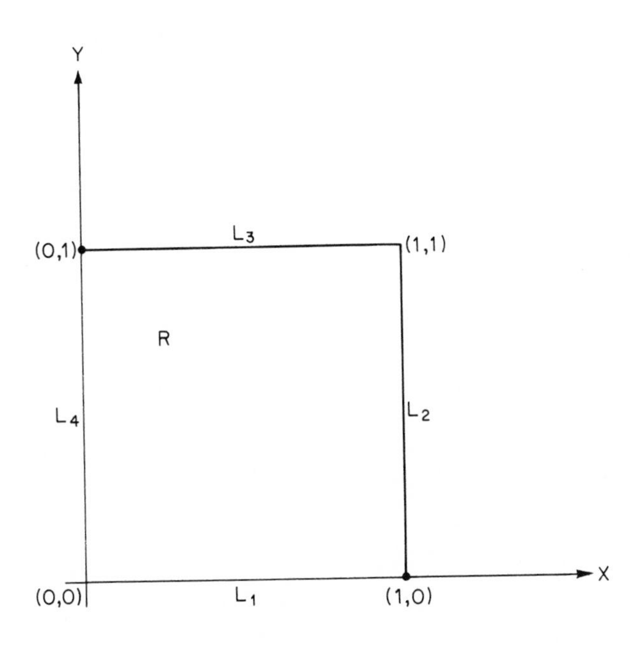

Figure 3.2

four sides of S be labeled L_1, L_2, L_3, L_4, as shown in Figure 3. 2, so that $S = L_1 + L_2 + L_3 + L_4$. If $f(x, y) = x^2y$ on S, then the resulting Dirichlet problem for

$$u_{xx} + u_{yy} - \frac{3}{y}u_y = 0$$

has a unique solution. If $f(x, y) = x - 3y^3$ on $S - L_1 = L_2 + L_3 + L_4$, then the resulting Dirichlet problem for

$$u_{xx} + u_{yy} + \frac{3}{y}u_y = 0$$

has a unique solution. However, if $f(x, y) = x - 3y^2$ on S, then the resulting Dirichlet problem for

$$u_{xx} + u_{yy} + \frac{1}{y}u_y = 0$$

may have no solution at all.

Again, because in general one does not know how to construct solutions of the problems formulated in Theorem 3.1, attention will be directed next toward numerical methods.

3.4. Difference Equation Approximations. At a point (x, y) consider the elliptic equation

(3.12) $$u_{xx} + u_{yy} + \frac{K}{y} u_y = 0, \quad K \text{ a non-zero constant}, \quad y \neq 0.$$

Let (x, y) be numbered zero and, as in Figure 2.1, let the four points $(x+h_1, y)$, $(x, y+h_2)$, $(x-h_3, y)$, $(x, y-h_4)$ be numbered $1, 2, 3, 4$, respectively. Set

(3.13) $$u_{xx} + u_{yy} + \frac{K}{y} u_y = \sum_0^4 \alpha_i u_i .$$

Substitution of finite Taylor expansions about (x, y) for u_1, u_2, u_3, u_4 and setting corresponding coefficients equal implies

$$\begin{aligned}
\alpha_0 + \alpha_1 + \alpha_2 + \alpha_3 + \alpha_4 &= 0 \\
h_1\alpha_1 - h_3\alpha_3 &= 0 \\
h_2\alpha_2 - h_4\alpha_4 &= \frac{K}{y} \\
\alpha_1 h_1^2 + \alpha_3 h_3^2 &= 2 \\
\alpha_2 h_2^2 + \alpha_4 h_4^2 &= 2 ,
\end{aligned}$$

the unique solution of which is

$$\alpha_0 = -\left[\frac{2}{h_1h_3} + \frac{2}{h_2h_4} + \frac{K(h_4 - h_2)}{yh_2h_4}\right]$$

$$\alpha_1 = \frac{2}{h_1(h_1+h_3)}, \qquad \alpha_2 = \frac{2y+h_4K}{yh_2(h_2+h_4)}$$

$$\alpha_3 = \frac{2}{h_3(h_1+h_3)}, \qquad \alpha_4 = \frac{2y-h_2K}{yh_4(h_2+h_4)} .$$

The difference equation approximation of (3.12) which then results is

$$(3.14) \quad -\left[\frac{2}{h_1h_3} + \frac{2}{h_2h_4} + \frac{K(h_4-h_2)}{yh_2h_4}\right] u_0 + \frac{2}{h_1(h_1+h_3)} u_1 + \frac{2y+h_4K}{yh_2(h_2+h_4)} u_2$$

$$+ \frac{2}{h_3(h_1+h_3)} u_3 + \frac{2y-h_2K}{yh_4(h_2+h_4)} u_4 = 0 .$$

3.5. Numerical Methods. In order to treat numerically the analytical problems described in Theorem 3.1, we shall, for simplicity, restrict ourselves to regions whose boundaries on the left and on the right, as shown in Figure 3.3, are vertical. For treatment of more general regions, see [171]. Of necessity, the discussion must be divided into two parts, one for the case $K < 1$ and the other for the case $K \geq 1$.

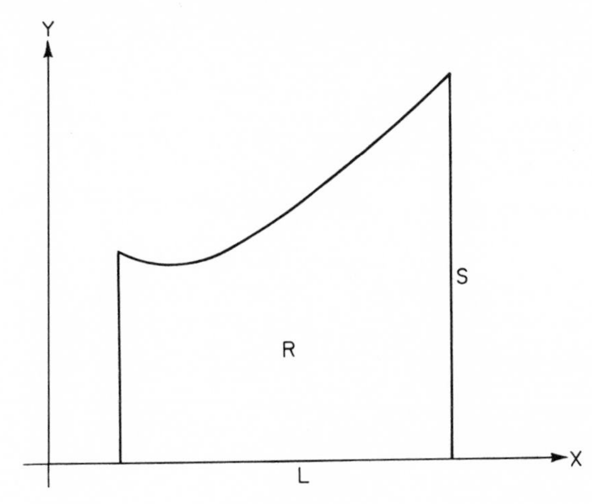

Figure 3.3

<u>Case 1. $K < 1$</u>. First, for $\sigma > 0$, let R_σ be that subregion of R which lies above the line $y = \sigma$ (see Figure 3.4). The effect now of limiting the discussion to the region R_σ is to eliminate the singularity of the coefficient $\frac{K}{y}$ in (3.12), for on R_σ the variable y cannot be made arbitrarily close to zero. Let the boundary of R_σ be S_σ. For $h > 0$ and for $(\bar{x}, \bar{y}) = (0, \sigma)$ construct and number the set of interior grid points $R_{\sigma, h}$ and the boundary grid points $S_{\sigma, h}$ in the fashion described previously.

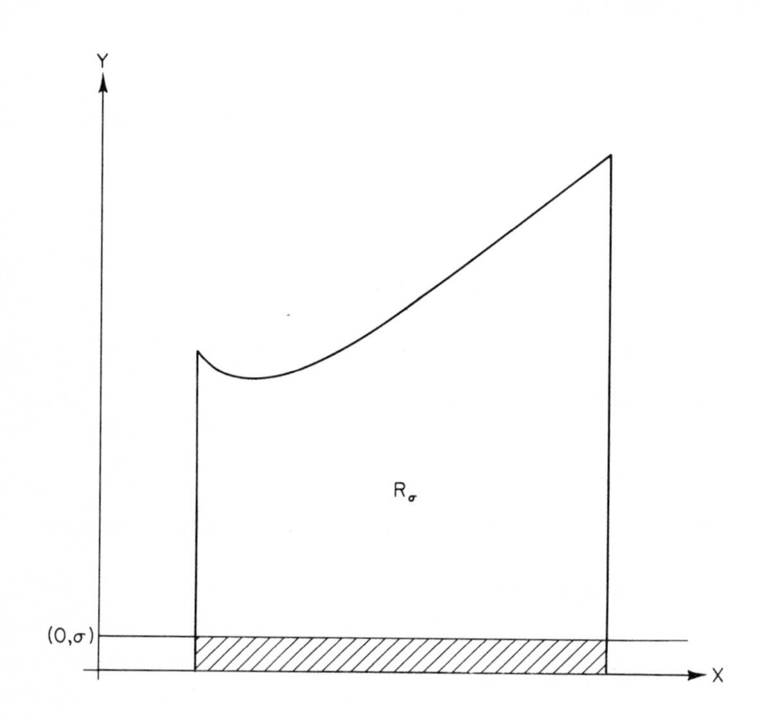

Figure 3.4

Now, since $f(x, y)$ is defined on all of S, if one sets

$$f(x, \sigma) = f(x, 0), \tag{3.15}$$

then f is defined at each point of $S_{\sigma, h}$. The effect of (3.15) is merely to take the values of f defined on L and to translate them vertically onto the portion of $y = \sigma$ which is above L. Application now at each point of $R_{\sigma,h}$ of (3.14) results in n linear algebraic equations in n unknowns, the solution of which constitutes the numerical solution. In order to assure a priori that this system has a unique solution, it is sufficient to have $\alpha_0 < 0$; $\alpha_i > 0$, $i = 1, 2, 3, 4$, and these will be valid if one selects h to satisfy

$$h|K| < 2\sigma \quad . \tag{3.16}$$

Example. Consider the square S with vertices (0, 0), (1, 0), (1, 1) and (0, 1). Let R be the interior of S. Consider the Dirichlet problem for

$$u_{xx} + u_{yy} - \frac{1}{y} u_y = 0$$

with boundary function $f(x, y) = x-y$ on S (see Figure 3.5). Let $\sigma = \frac{1}{4}$. Since $K = -1$, it follows from (3.16) that we also can choose $h = \frac{1}{4}$. The points of $R_{\sigma,h}$ are numbered 1-6 in Figure 3.5, while those of $S_{\sigma,h}$ are numbered 7-16. Since f is defined on S, it is known at the points 7-13. To define f at 14-16, we merely set

$$f_{14} = f(\frac{3}{4}, \frac{1}{4}) = f(\frac{3}{4}, 0) = \frac{3}{4}$$

$$f_{15} = f(\frac{1}{2}, \frac{1}{4}) = f(\frac{1}{2}, 0) = \frac{1}{2}$$

$$f_{16} = f(\frac{1}{4}, \frac{1}{4}) = f(\frac{1}{4}, 0) = \frac{1}{4} \ ,$$

so that f is now defined on all of $S_{\sigma,h}$.

Difference equation (3.14) would then be applied in the form

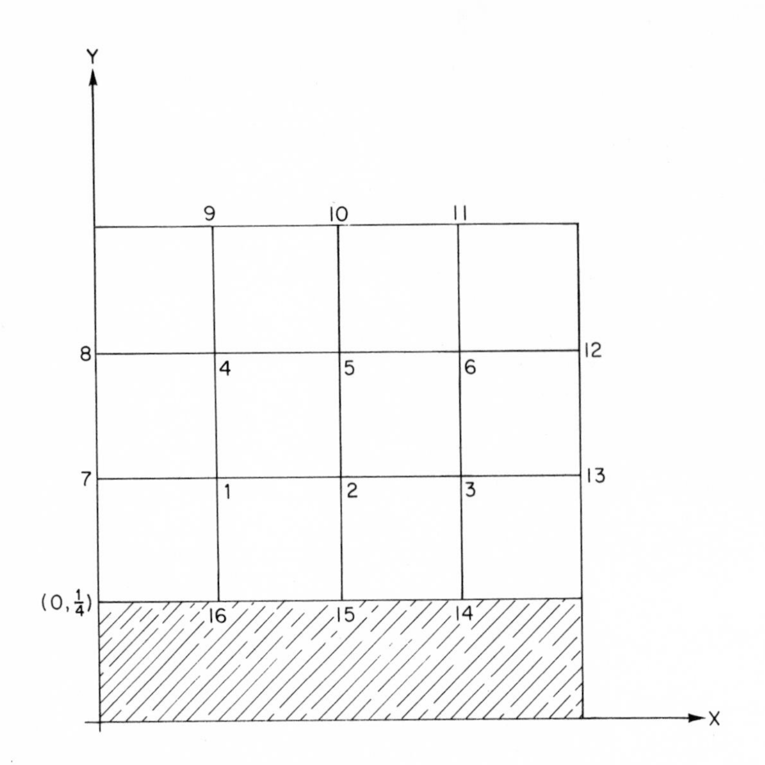

Figure 3.5

$$-64U_0 + 16\,U_1 + \frac{16y-2}{y}U_2 + 16\,U_3 + \frac{16y+2}{y}U_4 = 0$$

at each point of $R_{\sigma,h}$ to yield the linear algebraic system. Thus, for example, at the point numbered 3 in Figure 3.5, one would have

$$-\ 64U_3 + 16\,U_{13} + \frac{8-2}{1/2}U_6 + 16\,U_2 + \frac{8+2}{1/2}U_{14} = 0,$$

or, equivalently,

$$8U_2 - 32U_3 + 6U_6 = -9.$$

<u>Case 2. $K \geq 1$.</u> The method described above for Case 1 cannot be applied

to this case because f is <u>not</u> defined on S when $y = 0$. We now make an interesting observation. Suppose one were to contemplate applying (3.14) at each point of $S_{\sigma,h}$ for which $y = \sigma$. Then, since $K \geq 1$, there would be no value u_4 available. To account for this, let us set the coefficient of u_4 equal to zero, so that no u_4 would be necessary. Thus

$$\frac{2\sigma - h_2 K}{\sigma h_4 (h_2 + h_4)} = 0 .$$

However, for a region of the type shown in Figure 3.3, one has $h_2 = h$ for all sufficiently small h, so that

$$h = \frac{2\sigma}{K} . \tag{3.17}$$

For Case 2, then, the numerical method to be used is similar to that for Case 1 except that h is determined by (3.17), and, at each point of $S_{\sigma,h}$ which is in R and for which $y = \sigma$, we will apply (3.14).

<u>Example</u>. Consider a square with vertices (0, 0), (1, 0), (1, 1) and (0, 1). Let R be the interior of S. Let L be the interval on the X-axis joining (0, 0) and (1, 0). Consider the Dirichlet problem for

$$u_{xx} + u_{yy} + \frac{2}{y} u_y = 0$$

with boundary function $f(x, y) = x - y$ defined only on $S - L$ (see Figure 3.6). Take $\sigma = \frac{1}{5}$. Then, since $K = 2$, it follows from (3.17) that $h = \frac{1}{5}$. As shown in Figure 3.6, the points of $R_{\sigma,h}$ are numbered 1-12 while those of $S_{\sigma,h}$ are numbered 13-26. The difference equation (3.14) now has the form

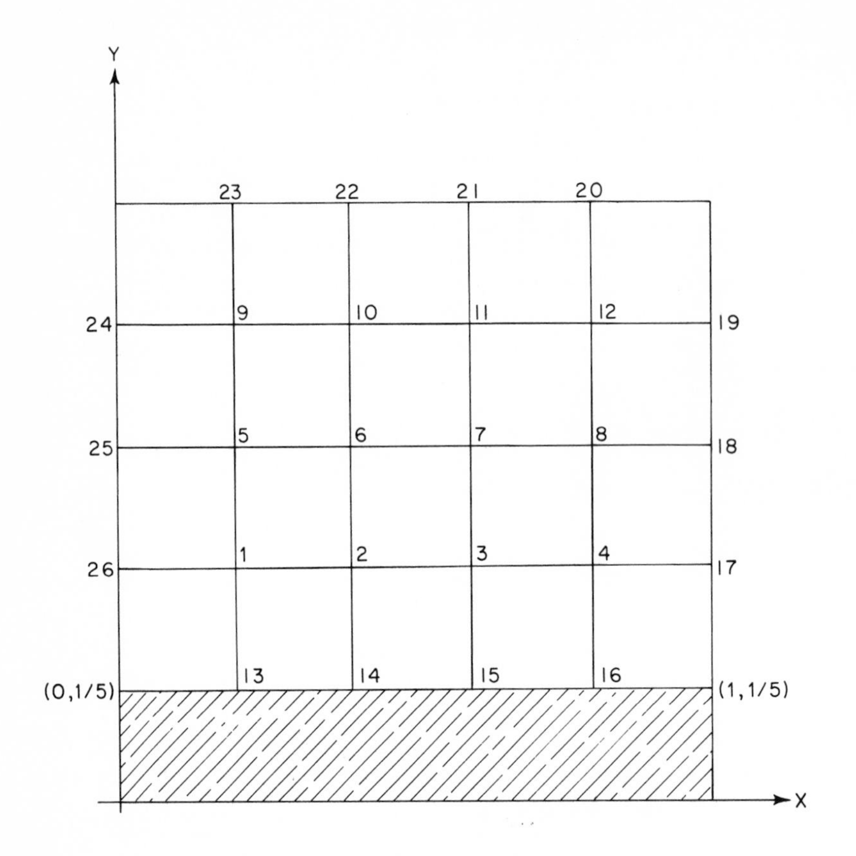

Figure 3.6

$$(3.18) \qquad -100u_0 + 25u_1 + \frac{50y+10}{2y}u_2 + 25u_3 + \frac{50y-10}{2y}u_4 = 0$$

and would be applied at each of the points 1 - 16 to yield 16 equations in 16 unknowns. Thus, for example, at the point numbered 7, in Figure 3.6, (3.18) would yield

$$-100U_7 + 25U_8 + \frac{50 \cdot \frac{3}{5} + 10}{2 \cdot \frac{3}{5}} U_{11} + 25U_6 + \frac{50 \cdot \frac{3}{5} - 10}{2 \cdot \frac{3}{5}} U_3 = 0 \ ,$$

or, equivalently,

$$-4U_7 + U_8 + \frac{4}{3}U_{11} + U_6 + \frac{2}{3}U_3 = 0 \ ,$$

while, at the point numbered 14, (3.14) would yield

$$-20\,U_{14} + 5\,U_{15} + 10U_2 + 5\,U_{13} = 0 .$$

Note, however, that application of (3.14) at the points numbered 13 and 16 would require the calculation of $f(0,\frac{1}{5})$ and $f(1,\frac{1}{5})$ from the given data, even though the points $(0,\frac{1}{5})$ and $(1,\frac{1}{5})$ are not included in the set $S_{\sigma,h}$. This minor inconvenience could be avoided by redefining $S_{\sigma,h}$, but this in turn might cause only greater confusion.

For a detailed treatment of several large scale examples by the methods of this section, see [171].

3.6. Remark. Attention will be directed next to problems in more than two dimensions. However, any time an n-dimensional problem can be reduced to an (n-1)-dimensional problem, this should be done in order to get the most efficient use out of the computer. It is worth noting now that the (two-dimensional) singular problems discussed in this lecture do, in fact, result from three dimensional problems with axial symmetry [171].

Lecture 4 - Linear Problems in Three Dimensions and the Classical Problem of Capacity

4.1. Extension to Three Dimensions. The numerical analysis developed thus far extends easily and naturally to linear problems in any number of dimensions. For clarity, however, we shall give the details only for three dimensional problems for the Laplace equation.

Let R be a bounded, three dimensional region and let S be its boundary. Let $f(x, y, z)$ be defined and continuous on S. Then the Dirichlet problem is that of finding a function $u(x, y, z)$ such that

(a) u satisfies on R the Laplace equation

$$\frac{\partial^2 u}{\partial x^2} + \frac{\partial^2 u}{\partial y^2} + \frac{\partial^2 u}{\partial z^2} = 0,$$

(b) $u \equiv f$ on S, and

(c) u is continuous on $R + S$.

Under several reasonable restrictions on S (see [74, 343], which though quite general are not as comprehensive as in the two dimensional case, it is known that the Dirichlet problem has a unique solution. As in Method D, in order to approximate this solution one need only construct for $h > 0$ finite three dimensional point sets R_h (interior grid points) in R and S_h (boundary grid points) in S, where in three dimensions each point of R_h has six neighbors (see Figure 4.1), and then solve the linear algebraic system which results by applying at each point (x, y, z)

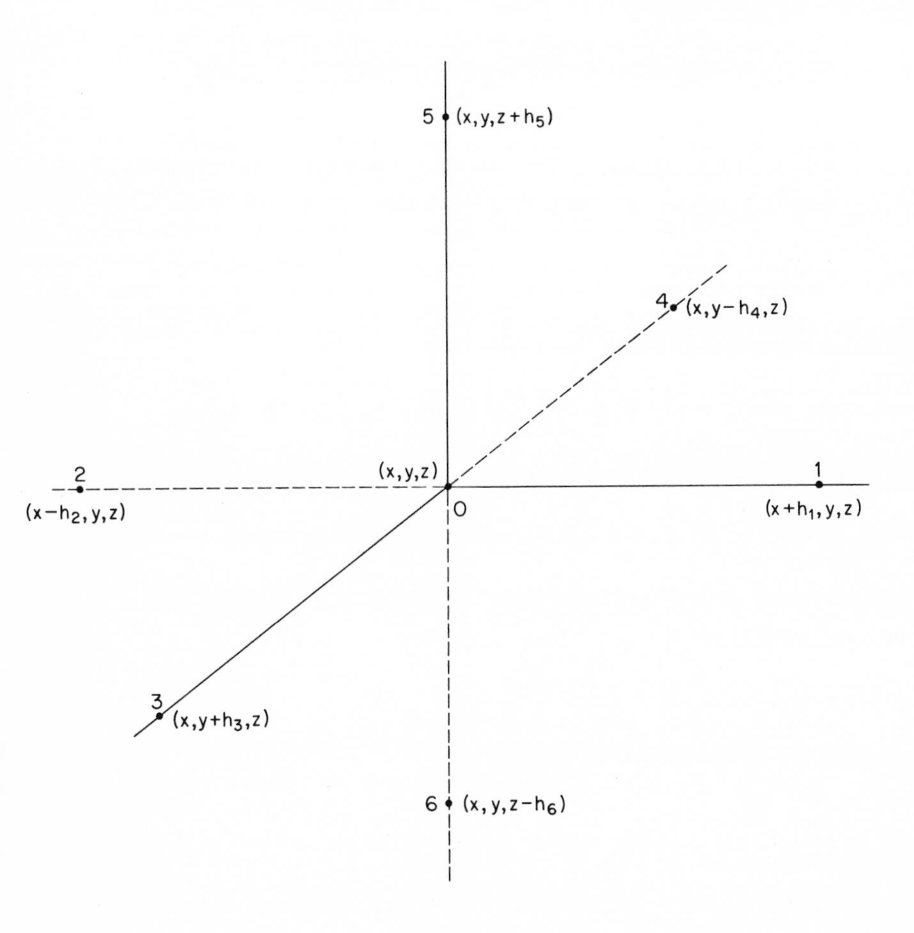

Figure 4.1

of R_h (see the notation in Figure 4.1) the difference equation

$$(4.1) \quad -2\left(\frac{1}{h_1h_2}+\frac{1}{h_3h_4}+\frac{1}{h_5h_6}\right)u_0+\frac{2}{h_1(h_1+h_2)}u_1+\frac{2}{h_2(h_1+h_2)}u_2+\frac{2}{h_3(h_3+h_4)}u_3$$

$$+\frac{2}{h_4(h_3+h_4)}u_4+\frac{2}{h_5(h_5+h_6)}u_5+\frac{2}{h_6(h_5+h_6)}u_6=0.$$

Note that difference analogue (4.1) of the three dimensional Laplace equation is a natural generalization of difference analogue (2.7) of the two dimensional Laplace equation, and that (4.1) can be constructed in the same fashion as was (2.7).

The exterior Dirichlet problem for the Laplace equation can be formulated as follows. Let R be a bounded, three dimensional region and let S be its boundary. Let R^* be the exterior of S and let $f(x, y, z)$ be defined and continuous on S. Then the exterior Dirichlet problem is that of finding a function $u(x, y, z)$ such that

(a) u satisfies on R^* the Laplace equation

$$\frac{\partial^2 u}{\partial x^2} + \frac{\partial^2 u}{\partial y^2} + \frac{\partial^2 u}{\partial z^2} = 0 ,$$

(b) $u \equiv f$ on S,

(c) u is continuous on $R^* + S$, and

(d) u is bounded on $R^* + S$.

Again [74, 343] it can be shown that, under rather general restrictions on S, the exterior Dirichlet problem has a unique solution.

Unfortunately, the numerical method which was applied to solve the exterior problem in two dimensions <u>does not extend</u> per se to three dimensions. With a simple modification, however, it will extend, and this will be explored next.

As in (2.22) - (2.23), inversion with respect to a unit sphere in three dimensions is given by

$$(4.2) \qquad x = \frac{\xi}{\xi^2+\eta^2+\nu^2}, \quad y = \frac{\eta}{\xi^2+\eta^2+\nu^2}, \quad z = \frac{\nu}{\xi^2+\eta^2+\nu^2}, \quad \xi^2+\eta^2+\nu^2 \neq 0 ,$$

or, equivalently, by

$$(4.3)\quad \xi = \frac{x}{x^2+y^2+z^2}, \quad \eta = \frac{y}{x^2+y^2+z^2}, \quad \nu = \frac{z}{x^2+y^2+z^2}, \quad x^2+y^2+z^2 \neq 0.$$

Consider now the following theorem (compare with Theorem 2.1).

<u>Theorem 4.1.</u> Let $u(x, y, z)$ be the solution of the exterior Dirichlet problem. Without loss of generality, assume that $(0, 0, 0)$ is in R. Under inversion with respect to, say, the unit sphere, let

$$R^* \to R^i$$

$$S \to S^i$$

$$(4.4)\quad u(x, y, z) = u\left(\frac{\xi}{\xi^2+\eta^2+\nu^2}, \frac{\eta}{\xi^2+\eta^2+\nu^2}, \frac{\nu}{\xi^2+\eta^2+\nu^2}\right) = V(\xi, \eta, \nu)$$

$$(4.5)\quad f(x, y, z) = f\left(\frac{\xi}{\xi^2+\eta^2+\nu^2}, \frac{\eta}{\xi^2+\eta^2+\nu^2}, \frac{\nu}{\xi^2+\eta^2+\nu^2}\right) = \mathcal{F}(\xi, \eta, \nu).$$

Define $v(\xi, \eta, \nu)$ and $F(\xi, \eta, \nu)$ by

$$(4.6)\quad v(\xi, \eta, \nu) = \frac{V(\xi, \eta, \nu)}{\sqrt{\xi^2+\eta^2+\nu^2}}$$

$$(4.7)\quad F(\xi, \eta, \nu) = \frac{\mathcal{F}(\xi, \eta, \nu)}{\sqrt{\xi^2+\eta^2+\nu^2}}.$$

Then $v(\xi, \eta, \nu)$ is the solution of the Dirichlet problem on $R^i + S^i$ with boundary function F, that is

(a) $$\frac{\partial^2 v}{\partial \xi^2} + \frac{\partial^2 v}{\partial \eta^2} + \frac{\partial^2 v}{\partial \nu^2} = 0, \quad \text{on } R^i,$$

(b) $v(\xi, \eta, \nu)$ is defined and continuous on $R^i + S^i$, and

(c) $v(\xi, \eta, \nu) \equiv F(\xi, \eta, \nu)$, on S^i.

For the proof see [343] .

With regard to solving the exterior Dirichlet problem numerically by first inverting with respect to the unit sphere, the implications of Theorem 4.1, and especially of (4.4) - (4.7), are that u, v, f and F are related by

$$u(x,y,z) = \left(\sqrt{\xi^2+\eta^2+\nu^2}\right)(v(\xi,\eta,\nu)) \tag{4.8}$$

$$f(x,y,z) = \left(\sqrt{\xi^2+\eta^2+\nu^2}\right)(F(\xi,\eta,\nu)) , \tag{4.9}$$

which are, indeed, different in character than the two dimensional relationships (2.24) and (2.25).

<u>4.2. The Classical Problem of Capacity.</u> Rather than merely give illustrative examples of the numerical solution of three dimensional problems, we shall at the same time consider a physical problem which is of long standing interest, which is exceptionally difficult to solve analytically, and which has application in such diverse fields as electron optics, antenna design, plasma dynamics, fluid dynamics, and electrostatics [173] .

If in the exterior Dirichlet problem one sets

$$f(x,y,z) \equiv 1$$

and if $\frac{\partial u}{\partial n}$ is the outward normal derivative on S of the solution of the resulting problem, then the capacity C of S is defined by the surface integral

$$C = -\frac{1}{4\pi} \iint_S \frac{\partial u}{\partial n} dA . \tag{4.10}$$

From, say, the electrostatic point of view, the capacity C of S is the total charge, which, in equilibrium on S, raises the potential of S to unity.

Unfortunately, for a given nonspherical S, the precise numerical value of C is, in general, so difficult to determine analytically that even the capacity of the unit cube has become a quantity of great interest. Mathematicians have approached such problems by means of isoperimetric inequalities, while physicists and engineers have been prone to apply infinite series techniques. The isoperimetric inequality approach requires special results for each S and yields upper and lower bounds for C which are rarely sharp. The infinite series approach usually requires very extensive tables, which are different for each S, and which may have to be so voluminous to attain a reasonable accuracy that the method becomes impractical.

We shall show next, then, how to apply the numerical methods outlined in Section 4.1 in a completely general and efficient way to estimate the capacities of various surfaces of physical interest, and the simple key to the entire method lies in the known result [181] that if u and v are related by (4.8), then the capacity C, given by (4.10), can be given alternately by

$$C = v(0, 0, 0). \tag{4.11}$$

4.3. Capacity of a Cube. Let S be the unit cube whose vertices are $(\frac{1}{2}, \frac{1}{2}, \frac{1}{2}), (\frac{1}{2}, \frac{1}{2}, -\frac{1}{2}), (\frac{1}{2}, -\frac{1}{2}, \frac{1}{2}), (-\frac{1}{2}, \frac{1}{2}, \frac{1}{2}), (\frac{1}{2}, -\frac{1}{2}, -\frac{1}{2}), (-\frac{1}{2}, \frac{1}{2}, -\frac{1}{2}),$

$(-\frac{1}{2}, -\frac{1}{2}, \frac{1}{2}), (-\frac{1}{2}, -\frac{1}{2}, -\frac{1}{2})$, as shown in Figure 4. 2. Then S^i, the map of S under inversion transformation (4. 2) or (4. 3), is a completely

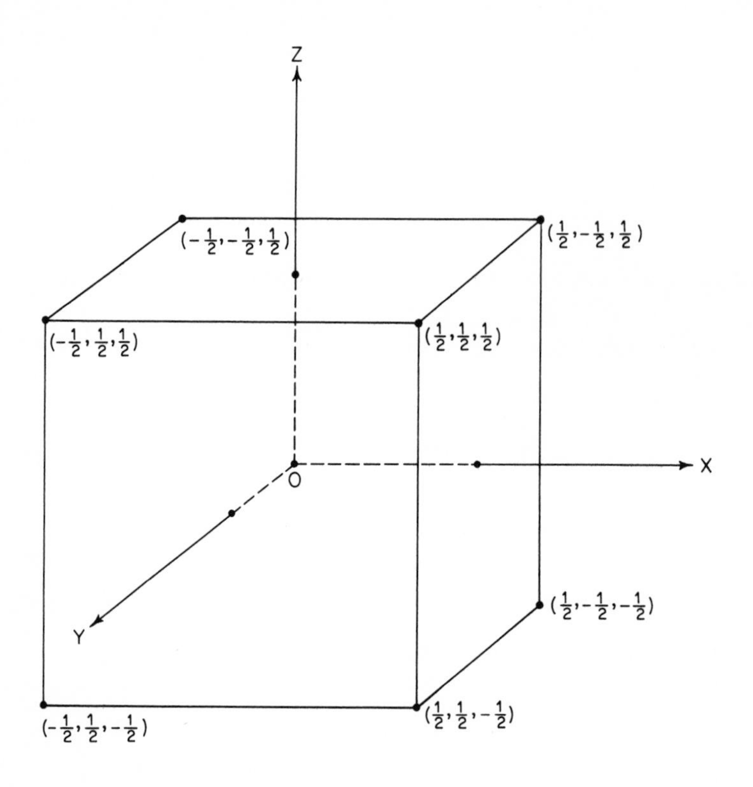

Figure 4.2

symmetric surface consisting of six partially spherical caps, the first octant of which is shown in Figure 4. 3. With boundary function $F(\xi, \eta, \nu) = (\xi^2 + \eta^2 + \nu^2)^{-1/2}$, the method outlined in Section 4. 1 was applied with grid size $h = 0.045$ and $w = 1.94$ to yield on the CDC 3600 in sixteen minutes the approximation

$$C = v(0, 0, 0) = 0.661.$$

By means of isoperimetric inequalities, the following upper and lower

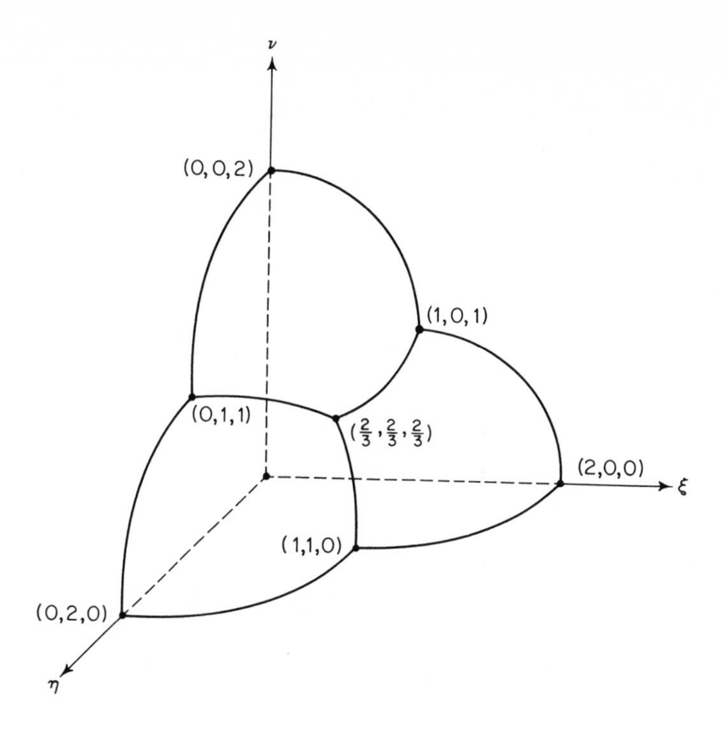

Figure 4.3

bounds on C had been obtained previously:

$$0.632 < C < 0.71055 \qquad \text{(see [354])}$$

$$0.654 < C < 0.668 \qquad \text{(see [338])}$$

$$C < 0.6626 \qquad \text{(see [331])}.$$

4.4. Capacity of a Lens. When two spheres have a nondegenerate intersection, the volume common to the spheres is called a lens. Without loss of generality, then, consider two spheres S_1 and S_2, with respective equations

$$S_1: \ (x-\alpha)^2 + y^2 + z^2 = \gamma_1^2, \quad \alpha > 0 \tag{4.12}$$

$$S_2: \ (x-\beta)^2 + y^2 + z^2 = \gamma_2^2, \quad \beta < 0, \tag{4.13}$$

with nondegenerate intersection. Assume also that, as shown in Figure 4.4, the circle of intersection of S_1 and S_2 lies in the YZ plane. Then

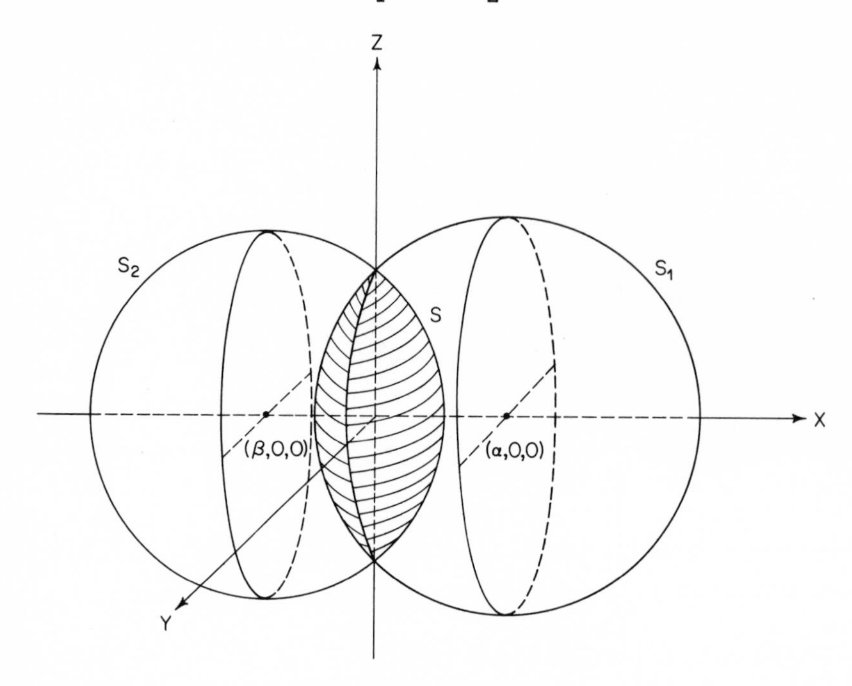

Figure 4.4

$$\gamma_1^2 - \alpha^2 = \gamma_2^2 - \beta^2 \tag{4.14}$$

and in Figure 4.4 the surface S of the resulting lens has been shaded. Under inversion (4.2), let $S_1 \to S_1^i$ and $S_2 \to S_2^i$, so that the equations of S_1^i and S_2^i are

$$S_1^i : \left(\xi + \frac{\alpha}{\gamma_1^2 - \alpha^2}\right)^2 + \eta^2 + \nu^2 = \frac{\gamma_1^2}{(\gamma_1^2 - \alpha^2)^2}, \tag{4.15}$$

$$S_2^i : \left(\xi + \frac{\beta}{\gamma_2^2 - \beta^2}\right)^2 + \eta^2 + \nu^2 = \frac{\gamma_2^2}{(\gamma_2^2 - \beta^2)^2}. \tag{4.16}$$

he graphs of S_1^i and S_2^i are shown in Figure 4. 5, where the shaded ortion is the map S^i of S.

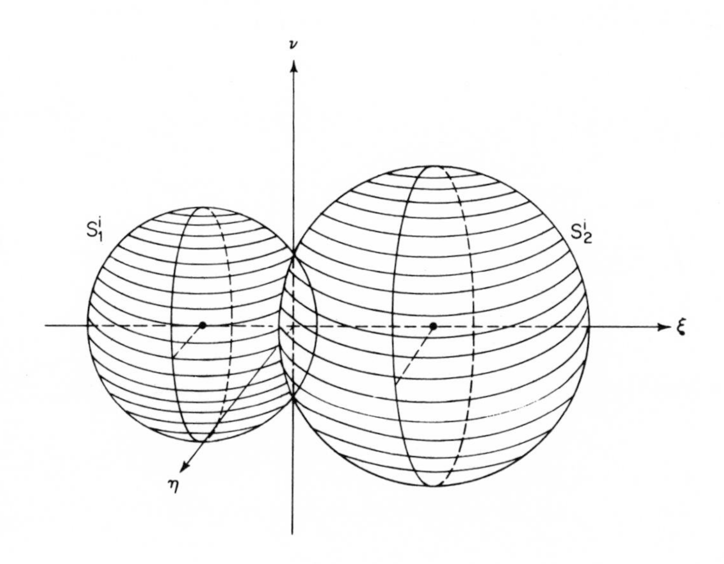

Figure 4.5

In the same spirit as for the cube, the numerical method was applied o the particular lens

$$S_1 : (x-4)^2 + y^2 + z^2 = 25 \tag{4.17}$$

$$S_2 : (x+2)^2 + y^2 + z^2 = 13 . \tag{4.18}$$

With a grid size $h = 0.04$, the approximation

$$C = v(0, 0, 0) = 2.29$$

vas obtained in four minutes.

By means of some highly specialized lens theorems, Herriot [194] ad shown previously that

$$2.205 \leq C \leq 3.183.$$

4.5. Capacity of a Torus. Consider finally the torus, or, as is known in antenna theory, the ring. Let a, b, c be three positive constants with $c \geq a$. Let the elliptic torus S, as shown in Figure 4.6, be generated by rotating the ellipse, whose equation in the XZ plane is

$$\frac{x^2}{a^2} + \frac{z^2}{b^2} = 1 \tag{4.19}$$

around the line whose equation in the XZ plane is $x = c$. The equation

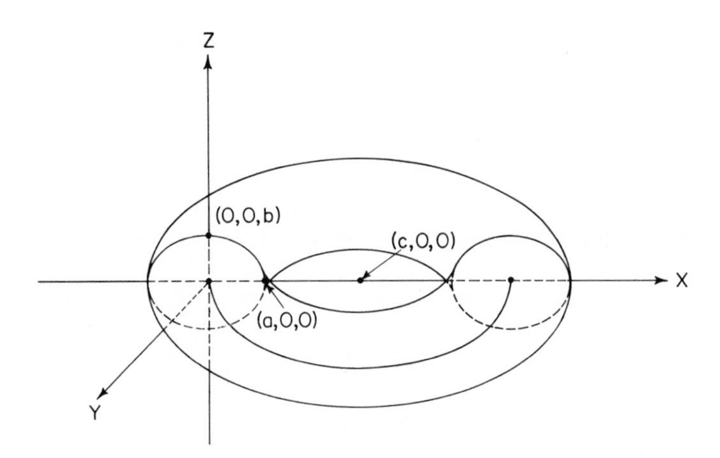

Figure 4.6

of the resulting elliptic torus is

$$\left(x^2 + y^2 + \frac{a^2}{b^2} z^2 - 2xc - a^2\right)^2 + \frac{4a^2c^2}{b^2}(z^2 - b^2) = 0\ . \tag{4.20}$$

Under inversion mapping (4.2), equation (4.20) transforms into

$$(4.21)\quad [\xi^2+\eta^2+\frac{a^2}{b^2}\nu^2-2c\xi(\xi^2+\eta^2+\nu^2)-a^2(\xi^2+\eta^2+\nu^2)^2]^2$$

$$+\frac{4a^2c^2}{b^2}[\nu^2(\xi^2+\eta^2+\nu^2)^2-b^2(\xi^2+\eta^2+\nu^2)^4] = 0 .$$

Now, instead of attempting to graph (4.21), we shall discuss the ata which must be incorporated into the computer program so that the apacity can be calculated easily.

First, the graph of (4.21) must be contained in some parallelopiped. ndeed, since either $(a, 0, 0)$ or $(0, 0, b)$ is the closest point on S to the rigin in X, Y, Z space, it follows that $(1/a, 0, 0)$ or $(0, 0, 1/b)$ is the urthest point on S^1 from the origin in ξ, η, ν space. Thus, S^1 is ounded by the cube with center at the origin, edges parallel to the oordinate axes, and edge length equal to $\max(2/a, 2/b)$. Of course, maller parallelopipeds can be constructed, but the cube so defined uffices for description of the computations. Second, the computer must ave some rule by which to determine whether a given point (ξ, η, ν) lies nside, on, or outside S^1, and this is decided as follows. The point $(\xi, \eta, \nu) = (0, 0, 0)$ lies inside S^1 by construction. A point $(\xi, \eta, \nu) \neq (0, 0, 0)$ lies on S^1 if it satisfies (4.21). Finally, a point $(\xi, \eta, \nu) \neq (0,0,0)$ ies inside S^1, provided

$$(4.22)\quad [\xi^2+\eta^2+\frac{a^2}{b^2}\nu^2-2c\xi(\xi^2+\eta^2+\nu^2)-a^2(\xi^2+\eta^2+\nu^2)^2]^2$$

$$+\frac{4a^2c^2}{b^2}[\nu^2(\xi^2+\eta^2+\nu^2)^2-b^2(\xi^2+\eta^2+\nu^2)^4] > 0,$$

while it lies outside S^1 if the inequality (4.22) is reversed.

Two cases of particular interest were considered when running examples. For a circular torus with $a = b = \sqrt{2}$, $c = 5$, and grid size $h = 0.036$, the approximation which resulted was

$$C = v(0,0,0) = 4.89. \tag{4.23}$$

The running time was 6 minutes. After constructing extensive tables of circular toroidal functions, Loh [265] used series methods to construct the estimate

$$C = 4.90. \tag{4.24}$$

Next, for an elliptic torus with $a = 1$, $b = 0.75$, $c = 1.1$, and grid size $h = 0.07$, the approximation which resulted was

$$C = v(0,0,0) = 1.7034. \tag{4.25}$$

The running time was 3 minutes. For this surface, the bounds attained thus far by means of isoperimetric inequalities yield no meaningful results, while the method of series involves such extensive computations that no effort at all has been made in this direction.

Lecture 5 - Mildly Nonlinear Elliptic Problems

5.1. Introduction. We return now to two dimensional problems but begin the study of nonlinear equations. The three prototype problems of the classes of elliptic equations to be considered are

$$(5.1) \qquad u_{xx} + u_{yy} = e^u \qquad \text{(radiation equation)}$$

$$(5.2) \qquad u_{xx} + u_{yy} = u^2 \qquad \text{(molecular interaction equation)}$$

$$(5.3) \qquad (1+u_y^2)u_{xx} - 2u_x u_y u_{xy} + (1+u_x^2)u_{yy} = 0 \qquad \text{(soap film equation)}$$

Equations (5.1) and (5.2) are called "mildly nonlinear" and will be studied in this lecture. Study of equation (5.3) will be deferred until Lecture 9.

If R is a simply connected, bounded region whose boundary S is piecewise regular, then on R any nonlinear equation of the form

$$(5.4) \qquad Au_{xx} + 2Bu_{xy} + Cu_{yy} = F(x, y, u, u_x, u_y)$$

where A, B, C are constants which satisfy at each point of R

$$A^2 + B^2 + C^2 \neq 0$$

is said to be mildly nonlinear on R. When (5.4) is of the particular elliptic form

$$(5.5) \qquad u_{xx} + u_{yy} = F(x, y, u),$$

where F is continuous, we shall explore the associated Dirichlet problem, that is, the problem of finding $u(x, y)$ which, for given $f(x, y)$ continuous on S, satisfies

(a) u is defined and continuous on $R + S$

(b) u satisfies (5. 5) on R, and

(c) $u \equiv f$ on S.

5. 2. A First Numerical Method. If one wishes to extend Method D to the Dirichlet problem for (5. 5), then it would be advantageous if solutions of (5. 5) had some of the properties of harmonic functions. A max-min property can indeed be established for functions which satisfy (5. 5) under the assumption [74] that, for all real values of x, y and u,

$$\frac{\partial F}{\partial u} \geq 0, \tag{5. 6}$$

and this will be assumed throughout this section. Note that equation (5. 1) satisfies (5. 6) but that equation (5. 2) does not. Method D need be modified now by only replacing linear difference equation (2. 7) with the nonlinear difference equation

$$-\left[\frac{2}{h_1h_3}+\frac{2}{h_2h_4}\right]u_0+\frac{2}{h_1(h_1+h_3)}u_1+\frac{2}{h_2(h_2+h_4)}u_2+\frac{2}{h_3(h_1+h_3)}u_3+\frac{2}{h_4(h_2+h_4)}u_4 = F(x, y, u_0), \tag{5. 7}$$

and the resulting method is mathematically respectable.

Example. Let S be the square with vertices (0, 0), (1, 0), (1, 1), (0, 1), and let R be the interior of S. On S define f by $f(x, y) = 0$. For $h = \frac{1}{3}$, the points of R_h, as shown in Figure 5. 1, are numbered 1, 2, 3, 4. If

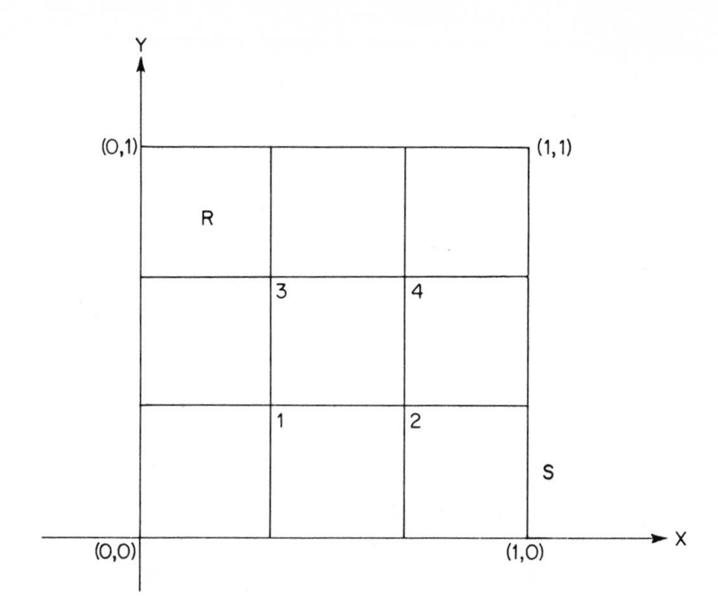

Figure 5.1

the equation defined on R is (5.1), then application of (5.7) at each point of R_h yields the system

$$-36U_1 + 9U_2 + 9U_3 = e^{U_1}$$

$$-36U_2 + 9U_4 + 9U_1 = e^{U_2}$$

$$-36U_3 + 9U_1 + 9U_4 = e^{U_3}$$

$$-36U_4 + 9U_3 + 9U_2 = e^{U_4}$$

This system can then be solved easily by the generalized Newton's method to yield the numerical solution.

For an example in which S was taken as the unit circle, R its interior, $f = x+2y$ and the equation (5.5) had the special form (5.1), the numerical method described above with $h = .1$ resulted in 410 nonlinear equations. On the CDC 3600, these equations were solved by the generalized Newton's method in just under 1 minute (see, e.g., [185]).

It should also be noted that the method outlined above applies equally well when (5.5) has the form

$$u_{xx} + u_{yy} = F(x, y, u, u_x, u_y)$$

with the additional supposition that F_{u_x} and F_{u_y} are bounded [171].

5.3. A Second Numerical Method. One can say that the method in Section 5.2 is something of a "hammer and tongs" method in which one applies the brute force of the computer in a direct fashion. Note however that equation (5.2) does not satisfy condition (5.6) and for it an alternate numerical method must be devised. This method, incidentally, will also be applicable to (5.1).

It is important to note first that the Dirichlet problem for (5.2) does not have a unique solution [350]. In order to consider a problem which does have a unique solution, physical considerations lead to the assumption on the boundary function f that $f(x, y) \geq 0$. It then follows [350] that the Dirichlet problem for (5.2) has a unique non-negative solution, and it is this solution that we shall attempt to approximate. The method to be described is simply a discretized form of Pohozaev's analytical method, in which he first reformulates the problem as an integral equation and then applies a Banach space form of Newton's method to solve the integral equation iteratively. The resulting analytical iteration formula for (5.5) would take the form

$$(5.8) \qquad \Delta u^{(n+1)} - F_u(x,y,u^{(n)})u^{(n+1)} = F(x,y,u^{(n)}) - F_u(x,y,u^{(n)})u^{(n)}, \quad n = 0,1,2,\ldots$$

which, one should observe, is a sequence of linear equations in $u^{(n+1)}$.

We shall illustrate the numerical method by considering a particular Dirichlet problem for equation (5.2).

Example. Let S be a square with vertices $(0,0)$, $(1,0)$, $(1,1)$ and $(0,1)$, and let R be the interior of S. On S defined $f(x,y) = 1$ and consider the resulting Dirichlet problem for the equation

$$(5.9) \qquad \Delta u = u^2.$$

The analytical form of (5.8) for equation (5.9) is

$$(5.10) \qquad \Delta u^{(n+1)} - 2u^{(n)}u^{(n+1)} = -[u^{(n)}]^2, \quad n = 0,1,2,\ldots .$$

In terms of the point arrangement shown in Figure 2.1, a discretized form of (5.10) is

$$(5.11) \qquad -\left[\frac{2}{h_1h_3} + \frac{2}{h_2h_4}\right]u_0^{(n+1)} + \frac{2}{h_1(h_1+h_3)}u_1^{(n+1)} + \frac{2}{h_2(h_2+h_4)}u_2^{(n+1)} + \frac{2}{h_3(h_1+h_3)}u_3^{(n+1)}$$
$$+ \frac{2}{h_4(h_2+h_4)}u_4^{(n+1)} - 2u_0^{(n)}u_0^{(n+1)} = -[u_0^{(n)}]^2, \quad n = 0,1,2,\ldots .$$

Now set $h = 1/3$, so that the points of R_h are numbered 1-4, as shown in Figure 5.2. Since $u \equiv f \equiv 1$ on S_h, there is no need to number the points of S_h. For $h = 1/3$, equation (5.11) reduces to

$$(5.12)\quad -36u_0^{(n+1)} + 9u_1^{(n+1)} + 9u_2^{(n+1)} + 9u_3^{(n+1)} + 9u_4^{(n+1)} - 2u_0^{(n)}u_0^{(n+1)} = -[u_0^{(n)}]^2, \qquad n = 0, 1, 2, \ldots .$$

Now, the entire method can be started only if $u_1^{(0)}, u_2^{(0)}, u_3^{(0)}$ and $u_4^{(0)}$ are given, for indeed only then can (5.12) be used in an iterative

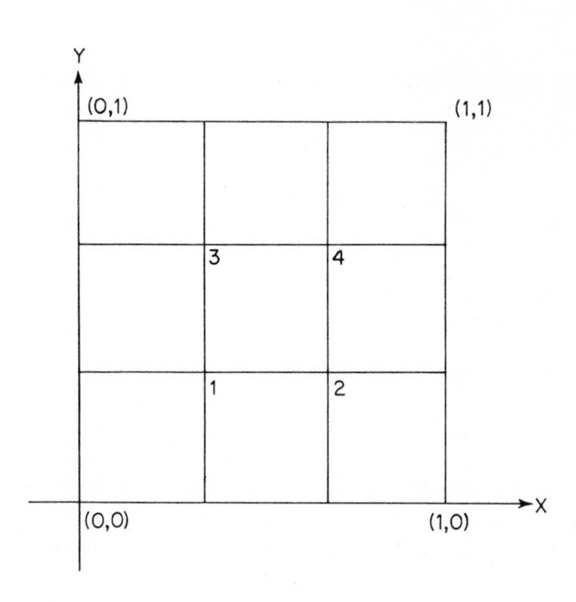

Figure 5.2

fashion. The values $u_1^{(0)}, u_2^{(0)}, u_3^{(0)}$ and $u_4^{(0)}$ are taken to be the numerical solution of the Dirichlet problem on $R + S$ with the given f but with the <u>Laplace</u> equation defined on R. Thus, $u_1^{(0)}, u_2^{(0)}, u_3^{(0)}$ and $u_4^{(0)}$ are determined by Method D, and in this case turn out to be

$$(5.13)\qquad u_1^{(0)} = u_2^{(0)} = u_3^{(0)} = u_4^{(0)} = 1.$$

Next, one applies (5.12) at each of the points 1, 2, 3 and 4 to yield the four equations

$$-36u_1^{(1)} + 9u_2^{(1)} + 9u_3^{(1)} + 9 + 9 - 2u_1^{(0)}u_1^{(1)} = -[u_1^{(0)}]^2$$

$$-36u_2^{(1)} + 9 + 9u_4^{(1)} + 9u_3^{(1)} + 9 - 2u_2^{(0)}u_2^{(1)} = -[u_2^{(0)}]^2$$

$$-36u_3^{(1)} + 9u_4^{(1)} + 9 + 9 + 9u_1^{(1)} - 2u_3^{(0)}u_3^{(1)} = -[u_3^{(0)}]^2$$

$$-36u_4^{(1)} + 9 + 9 + 9u_3^{(1)} + 9u_2^{(1)} - 2u_4^{(0)}u_4^{(1)} = -[u_4^{(0)}]^2 ,$$

which upon simplification and insertion of (5.13) yields the system

$$-38u_1^{(1)} + 9u_2^{(1)} + 9u_3^{(1)} = -19$$

$$-38u_2^{(1)} + 9u_4^{(1)} + 9u_3^{(1)} = -19$$

$$-38u_3^{(1)} + 9u_4^{(1)} + 9u_1^{(1)} = -19$$

$$-38u_4^{(1)} + 9u_3^{(1)} + 9u_2^{(1)} = -19 .$$

Solution of this system by the generalized Newton's method yields the values for $u_1^{(1)}, u_2^{(1)}, u_3^{(1)}, u_4^{(1)}$. Knowing these one can then find $u_1^{(2)}$, $u_2^{(2)}, u_3^{(2)}, u_4^{(2)}$ by applying (5.12) with $n = 1$ to each of the points 1, 2, 3, 4 in Figure 5.2 to yield the system

$$-36u_1^{(2)} + 9u_2^{(2)} + 9u_3^{(2)} + 9 + 9 - 2u_1^{(1)}u_1^{(2)} = -[u_1^{(1)}]^2$$

$$-36u_2^{(2)} + 9 + 9u_4^{(2)} + 9u_3^{(2)} + 9 - 2u_2^{(1)}u_2^{(2)} = -[u_2^{(1)}]^2$$

$$-36u_3^{(2)} + 9u_4^{(2)} + 9 + 9 + 9u_1^{(2)} - 2u_3^{(1)}u_3^{(2)} = -[u_3^{(1)}]^2$$

$$-36u_4^{(2)} + 9 + 9 + 9u_3^{(2)} + 9u_2^{(2)} - 2u_4^{(1)}u_4^{(2)} = -[u_4^{(1)}]^2 .$$

Substituting into this system of the known values $u_1^{(1)}, u_2^{(1)}, u_3^{(1)}, u_4^{(1)}$, and then solving by the generalized Newton's method yields readily the values $u_1^{(2)}, u_2^{(2)}, u_3^{(2)}, u_4^{(2)}$.

In the fashion described above, the iteration continues until a value k is reached for which $u_1^{(k)} = u_1^{(k+1)}$, $u_2^{(k)} = u_2^{(k+1)}$, $u_3^{(k)} = u_3^{(k+1)}$, $u_4^{(k)} = u_4^{(k+1)}$, and the approximate solution is taken to be $u_1^{(k)}, u_2^{(k)}, u_3^{(k)}, u_4^{(k)}$.

It is worth noting that the method developed in this section for a nonlinear problem is actually based on solving a sequence of linear problems, and that it is known that the method has firm mathematical basis [171].

Lecture 6 - Mildly Nonlinear Parabolic Problems

6.1. Introduction. In this lecture we shall initiate some numerical studies for initial-boundary problems for linear and nonlinear heat equations by means of boundary value techniques. Attention will be restricted to problems either for which asymptotic estimates are available or for which periodic solutions are known to exist. For the sake of consistency with the literature in this field, the variable y will be changed to t, thereby indicating the time dependence of solutions.

6.2. The Initial-Boundary Value Problem. The problems to be considered here will all have the following form. (Generalizations to curved boundaries and to higher dimensions follow in a natural way.)

For a given positive real number a, let I be the set of real numbers x which satisfy $0 \le x \le a$ and let R be the set of (x,t) for which $0 < x < a$ and $t > 0$. Let there be given three functions $\chi(x)$ for x in I, $\phi_1(t)$ for $t \ge 0$, and $\phi_2(t)$ for $t \ge 0$. On R consider the parabolic partial differential equation

$$u_{xx} - u_t = f(x, t, u, u_x). \tag{6.1}$$

Then the initial-boundary value problem is that of finding on R a solution $u(x,t)$ of (6.1) which is continuous at each (x,t) for which x is in I and $t \ge 0$ and which satisfies

$$u(x, 0) \equiv \chi(x), \quad 0 \le x \le a \qquad \text{(initial condition)} \tag{6.2}$$

$$u(0, t) \equiv \phi_1(t), \quad t \ge 0 \qquad \text{(boundary condition)} \tag{6.3}$$

(6. 4) $\quad u(a,t) \equiv \phi_2(t), \quad t \geq 0 \quad$ (boundary condition).

Under various assumptions on f, χ, ϕ_1, and ϕ_2, existence and uniqueness theorems are known [60, 137, 165]. But because again no general analytical technique is available to solve initial-boundary problem (6. 1) - (6. 4), attention will be directed to a numerical method for approximating a solution.

6. 3. A Parabolic Difference Approximation.

In this section we will construct a useful difference approximation which will render certain associated matrices "mildly" diagonally dominant. The value of diagonal dominance, which was present in a strong form for elliptic problems, cannot be underestimated when solving systems of algebraic equations by iteration.

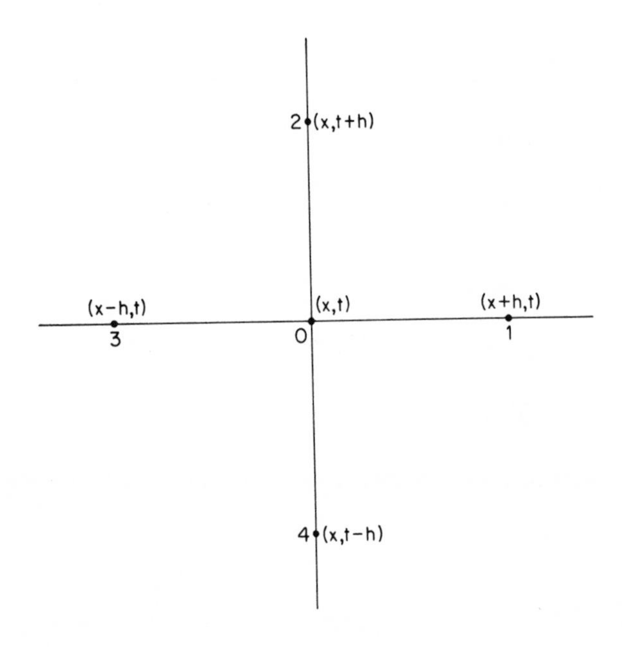

Figure 6.1

Consider the parabolic differential operator L defined by

$$L[u] \equiv u_{xx} - u_t. \tag{6.5}$$

For $h > 0$, let the points $(x, t), (x+h, t), (x, t+h), (x-h, t), (x, t-h)$ be denoted, respectively, by $0, 1, 2, 3, 4$, as shown in Figure 6.1. Let us seek to determine $\alpha_0, \alpha_1, \alpha_2, \alpha_3, \alpha_4$ such that at (x, y)

$$u_{xx} - u_t \equiv \sum_{i=0}^{4} \alpha_i u_i . \tag{6.6}$$

For this purpose, assume that u at each of the points numbered $1, 2, 3, 4$ can be developed in a Taylor expansion about the point numbered 0, so that

$$\begin{aligned}
(u_{xx} - u_t)|_0 &\equiv \sum_{i=0}^{4} \alpha_i u_i \\
&\equiv u_0(\alpha_0 + \alpha_1 + \alpha_2 + \alpha_3 + \alpha_4) \\
&+ u_x(h\alpha_1 - h\alpha_3) \\
&+ u_t(h\alpha_2 - h\alpha_4) \\
&+ \frac{u_{xx}}{2}(h^2\alpha_1 + h^2\alpha_3) \\
&+ \frac{u_{tt}}{2}(h^2\alpha_2 + h^2\alpha_4) \\
&+ \sum_{1}^{4} [O(\alpha_i h^3)]
\end{aligned}$$

In the above identity, setting corresponding coefficients equal yields

$$
\begin{aligned}
\alpha_0 + \alpha_1 + \alpha_2 + \alpha_3 + \alpha_4 &= 0 \\
h\alpha_1 \qquad - h\alpha_3 \qquad &= 0 \\
h\alpha_2 \qquad - h\alpha_4 &= -1 \\
\frac{h^2}{2}\alpha_1 \qquad + \frac{h^2}{2}\alpha_3 \qquad &= 1 \\
\frac{h^2}{2}\alpha_2 \qquad + \frac{h^2}{2}\alpha_4 &= 0 ,
\end{aligned}
$$

from which it follows that

(6.7) $$\alpha_0 = -\frac{2}{h^2}, \quad \alpha_1 = \alpha_3 = \frac{1}{h^2}, \quad \alpha_2 = -\alpha_4 = -\frac{1}{2h} .$$

Thus, (6.6) takes the form

(6.8) $$u_{xx} - u_t = -\frac{2}{h^2}u_0 + \frac{1}{h^2}u_1 - \frac{1}{2h}u_2 + \frac{1}{h^2}u_3 + \frac{1}{2h}u_4 + O(h) .$$

The difference operator

(6.9) $$L_h[u] = -\frac{2}{h^2}u_0 + \frac{1}{h^2}u_1 - \frac{1}{2h}u_2 + \frac{1}{h^2}u_3 + \frac{1}{2h}u_4$$

will be called an approximation of the differential operator

(6.10) $$L[u] = u_{xx} - u_t$$

The difference operator (6.9) is called mildly (diagonally) dominant for all values of h which imply the validity of the inequalities

$$|\alpha_0| > |\alpha_i| , \qquad i = 1, 2, 3, 4 .$$

6.4. A Numerical Method. A numerical method for approximating a solution of initial-boundary value problem (6.1) - (6.4) proceeds as follows Illustrative examples and examples typical of those run on the CDC 3600 will be presented after the method is described in complete generality.

For two fixed positive integers n and N, let $h = \frac{a}{n}$ and let T be the set of points (x, Nh), where $0 \leq x \leq a$. Let S_1 be the set of points $(0, y)$ for which $0 \leq y \leq Nh$ and let S_2 be the set of points (a, y) for which $0 \leq y \leq Nh$. Finally, set $S = I + T + S_1 + S_2$ (see Figure 6.2) and let R^* be the interior of S.

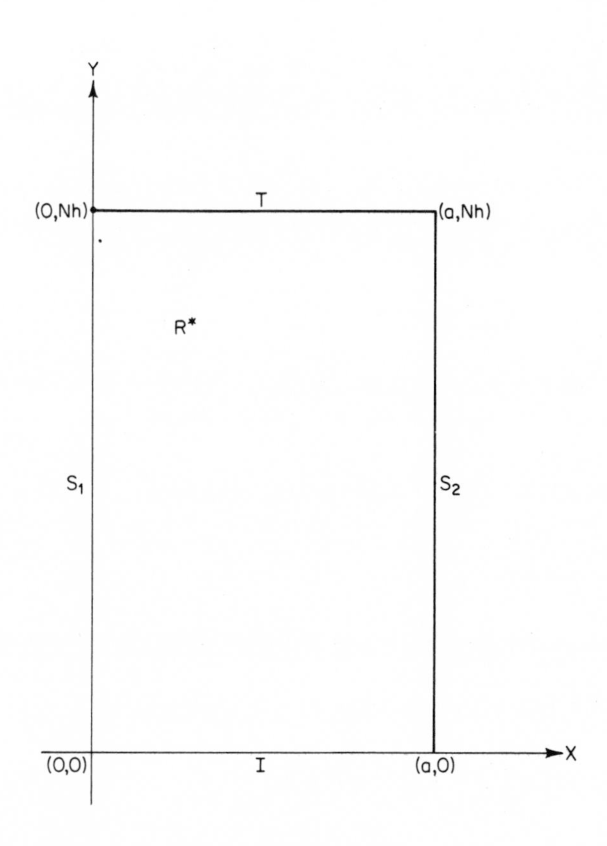

Figure 6.2

For the grid size h and with $(0, 0)$ a lattice point construct and number in the usual way the interior grid points R_h^* and the boundary grid points S_h. Approximate u on T by means of an asymptotic estimate or by some periodicity property possessed by u (see, e.g., [137, 202, 355] and the examples which follow). At each point in R_h^* select a difference approximation $u_{x,i}$ of u_x and write down the difference equation

$$(6.11)\qquad -\frac{2}{h^2}u_0 + \frac{1}{h^2}u_1 - \frac{1}{2h}u_2 + \frac{1}{h^2}u_3 + \frac{1}{2h}u_4 = f(x, t, u_0, u_{x,i}) .$$

There results a system of, say, k equations in the k unknowns $u_1, u_2, \ldots, u_k$, the solution of which consistutes the numerical solution.

Example 1. For $a = 1$, consider the initial-boundary value problem defined by

$$(6.12)\qquad u_{xx} - u_t = xu_x$$

$$(6.13)\qquad \chi(x) = x \quad , \quad 0 \leq x \leq 1$$

$$(6.14)\qquad \phi_1(t) = 0 \quad , \quad t \geq 0$$

$$(6.15)\qquad \phi_2(t) = e^{-t} , \quad t \geq 0 .$$

First note [137] that as $t \to \infty$, (6.12), (6.14) and (6.15) imply the steady state boundary value problem

$$(6.16)\qquad \frac{d^2u}{dx^2} - x\frac{du}{dx} = 0$$

$$(6.17)\qquad u(0) = 0$$

$$(6.18)\qquad u(1) = 0 ,$$

the solution of which is $u = 0$. Thus

$$\lim_{t \to \infty} u(x,t) = 0, \quad 0 < x < 1. \tag{6.19}$$

Now, let us select $h = \frac{1}{3}$ and $Nh = 2$. Then the ten resulting grid points in R_h^* are numbered $1, 2, \ldots, 10$, as shown in Figure 6.3.

From (6.13) - (6.15) one has first that

$$\begin{array}{lll} u(0,2) = 0 & u(0,\frac{1}{3}) = 0 & u(1,\frac{2}{3}) = e^{-2/3} \\ u(0,\frac{5}{3}) = 0 & u(0,0) = 0 & u(1,1) = e^{-1} \\ u(0,\frac{4}{3}) = 0 & u(\frac{1}{3},0) = \frac{1}{3} & u(1,\frac{4}{3}) = e^{-4/3} \\ u(0,1) = 0 & u(\frac{2}{3},0) = \frac{2}{3} & u(1,\frac{5}{3}) = e^{-5/3} \\ u(0,\frac{2}{3}) = 0 & u(1,0) = 1 & u(1,2) = e^{-2} \\ & u(1,\frac{1}{3}) = e^{-1/3} & \end{array} \tag{6.20}$$

and, from (6.19), we approximate u on the line $t = 2$ by

$$u(x,2) = 0, \quad 0 < x < 1. \tag{6.21}$$

Consider next a difference analogue of (6.12), or, equivalently, of

$$u_{xx} - u_t - xu_x = 0. \tag{6.22}$$

For an arrangement of points like that shown in Figure 6.1, the differential operator (6.5) can be approximated by the difference operator (6.9). In (6.8) the coefficient $-\frac{2}{h^2}$ of u_0 is greater in absolute value than the other coefficients and is negative. In order to preserve this mild dominance and negativeness, we select the central difference approximation

$$u_x = \frac{u_1 - u_3}{2h}, \tag{6.23}$$

for then substitution of (6. 8) and (6. 23) into (6. 22) yields the mildly dominant difference equation approximation

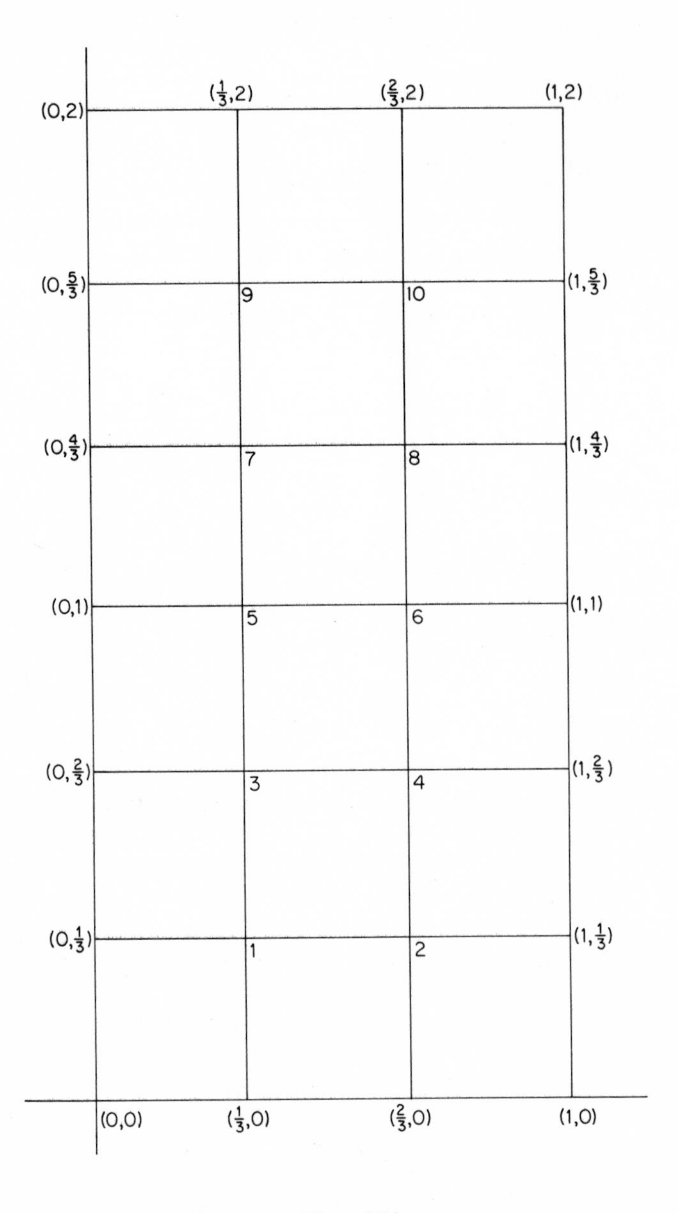

Figure 6.3

(6. 24) $$-\frac{2}{h^2}u_0 + \frac{1}{h^2}u_1 - \frac{1}{2h}u_2 + \frac{1}{h^2}u_3 + \frac{1}{2h}u_4 - x\left(\frac{u_1 - u_3}{2h}\right) = 0$$

of (6. 22). For convenience (6. 24) is rewritten in the following equivalent form:

(6. 25) $$-2u_0 + \left(1 - \frac{xh}{2}\right)u_1 - \frac{h}{2}u_2 + \left(1 + \frac{xh}{2}\right)u_3 + \frac{h}{2}u_4 = 0.$$

Since in the present example $h = \frac{1}{3}$, (6. 25) reduces to

(6. 26) $$-2u_0 + \left(1 - \frac{x}{6}\right)u_1 - \frac{1}{6}u_2 + \left(1 + \frac{x}{6}\right)u_3 + \frac{1}{6}u_4 = 0 .$$

Application of (6. 26) at the point numbered 1 in Figure (6. 3) implies

$$-2u_1 + \left(1 - \frac{1}{18}\right)u_2 - \frac{1}{6}u_3 + \left(1 + \frac{1}{18}\right)u\left(0, \frac{1}{3}\right) + \frac{1}{6}u\left(\frac{1}{3}, 0\right) = 0$$

or, equivalently,

(6. 27) $$-2u_1 + \frac{17}{18}u_2 - \frac{1}{6}u_3 = -\frac{1}{18} .$$

Similarly, application of (6. 26) at the points numbered $2, 3, \ldots, 10$ and use of (6. 20) and (6. 21) implies readily that

(6. 28) $$-2u_2 - \frac{1}{6}u_4 + \frac{10}{9}u_1 = -\frac{8}{9}e^{-1/3} - \frac{1}{9}$$

(6. 29) $$-2u_3 + \frac{17}{18}u_4 - \frac{1}{6}u_5 + \frac{1}{6}u_1 = 0$$

(6. 30) $$-2u_4 - \frac{1}{6}u_6 + \frac{10}{9}u_3 + \frac{1}{6}u_2 = -\frac{8}{9}e^{-2/3}$$

(6. 31) $$-2u_5 + \frac{17}{18}u_6 - \frac{1}{6}u_7 + \frac{1}{6}u_3 = 0$$

(6. 32) $$-2u_6 - \frac{1}{6}u_8 + \frac{10}{9}u_5 + \frac{1}{6}u_4 = -\frac{8}{9}e^{-1}$$

(6. 33) $$-2u_7 + \frac{17}{18}u_8 - \frac{1}{6}u_9 + \frac{1}{6}u_5 = 0$$

(6. 34) $$-2u_8 - \frac{1}{6}u_{10} + \frac{10}{9}u_7 + \frac{1}{6}u_6 = -\frac{8}{9}e^{-4/3}$$

$$(6.35) \qquad -2u_9 + \frac{17}{18}u_{10} + \frac{1}{6}u_7 = 0$$

$$(6.36) \qquad -2u_{10} + \frac{10}{9}u_9 + \frac{1}{6}u_8 = -\frac{8}{9}e^{-5/3}$$

The solution of system (6.27) - (6.36) was found easily by the generalized Newton's method and differed on R_h from the exact solution $u = xe^{-t}$ of (6.12) - (6.15) by at most two decimal places.

Example 2. Example 1 was repeated with $h = \frac{1}{15}$, $Nh = 30$. The resulting system of 6286 equations was solved on the CDC 3600 by the generalized Newton's method with $w = 1.3$ and with zero initial vector in 6 minutes and one second. The numerical solution agreed with the exact solution to at least five decimals, and,on the average, to ten decimal places.

Example 3. For $a = 1$, consider the initial-boundary problem defined by (6.13), (6.14), (6.15) and

$$(6.37) \qquad u_{xx} - u_t = u + u^3 - x^3e^{-3t}.$$

Proceeding in the same spirit as in Examples 1 and 2 but with (6.37) replaced by

$$(6.38) \qquad -2u_0 - h^2u_0 - h^2u_0^3 + u_1 - \frac{h}{2}u_2 + u_3 + \frac{h}{2}u_4 = -h^2x^3e^{-3t}$$

and with $h = \frac{1}{15}$ and $T = 30$, the resulting system of 6286 nonlinear equations was solved on the CDC 3600 by the generalized Newton's method with $w = 1.3$ and with zero initial vector in 6 minutes and three seconds. Since the exact solution of the given problem is

$$u = xe^{-t},$$

it was determined that the numerical solution differed from the analytical solution to at least five decimal places and, on the average, to ten decimal places.

With regard to this last example, it should be noted that the implication

$$\frac{\partial f}{\partial u} = \frac{\partial}{\partial u}(u + u^3 - x^3 e^{-3t}) = 1 + 3u^2 > 0$$

is most useful in establishing that the given initial-boundary value problem for (6. 37) has a unique solution and that the asymptotic behavior of the solution can be deduced in the fashion described in Example 1 (see [137]).

Example 4. For $a = \pi$, consider the initial-boundary problem defined by

(6. 39) $$u_{xx} - u_t = -\sin x(\sin t + \cos t)$$

(6. 40) $$\chi(x) = 0, \qquad 0 \le x \le \pi$$

(6. 41) $$\phi_1(t) = 0, \qquad t \ge 0$$

(6. 42) $$\phi_2(t) = 0, \qquad t \ge 0$$

Since, in (6. 39), $(\sin t + \cos t)$ has period 2π, we seek a solution of (6. 39) - (6. 42) which is of period 2π in t (see [355]). Thus, in addition to (6. 39) - (6. 42), we assume

(6. 43) $$u(x, 2\pi) = 0$$

and now proceed in the same spirit as in Examples 1 - 3, but with Nh always equal to 2π. With $h = \frac{\pi}{20}$, the resulting system of 741 equations was solved on the CDC 3600 with $w = 1.3$ and with zero initial vector in 1 minute, 54 seconds. Since the exact solution of (6.39) - (6.42) is

$$u = \sin x \sin t,$$

it was determined that the numerical solution differed from the analytical solution to at most three decimal places.

Finally, it should be noted that research to develop the mathematical bases for the method of this lecture is at present in progress.

Lecture 7 - Mildly Nonlinear Hyperbolic Problems

7.1. Introduction. In this lecture we will initiate some numerical studies for initial-boundary problems for wave equations by means of boundary value techniques. The approach will be similar in spirit to that of Lectures 5 and 6. Attention will be restricted to problems either for which asymptotic estimates are available or for which periodic solutions are known to exist. Again for the sake of consistency with the literature, the variable y will be changed to t to indicate the time dependence of solutions.

7.2. The Initial-Boundary Value Problem. The problems to be considered will all have the following form. (Generalizations to curved initial strips and to higher dimensions follow in a natural way.)

For a given positive real number a, let I be the set of real numbers x which satisfy $0 \leq x \leq a$ and let R be the set of points (x, t) whose coordinates satisfy $0 < x < a$ and $t > 0$. Let there be given four functions $\chi_1(x)$ for x in I, $\chi_2(x)$ for x in I, $\phi_1(t)$ for $t \geq 0$, and $\phi_2(t)$ for $t \geq 0$. On R, consider the hyperbolic equation

(7.1) $$u_{xx} - u_{tt} = f(x, t, u, u_x, u_t) .$$

Then the initial-boundary value problem is that of finding a function $u(x, t)$ which is a solution of (7.1) on R, which is continuous at each (x, t) for which $0 \leq x \leq a$ and $t \geq 0$, and which satisfies

$$(7.2) \qquad u(x,0) \equiv \chi_1(x) \quad , \quad x \text{ in } I$$

$$(7.3) \qquad \frac{\partial u(x,0)}{\partial t} \equiv \chi_2(x), \quad x \text{ in } I$$

initial conditions

$$(7.4) \qquad u(0,t) \equiv \phi_1(t), \qquad t \geq 0$$

$$(7.5) \qquad u(a,t) \equiv \phi_2(t), \qquad t \geq 0$$

boundary conditions .

Under various assumptions on f, χ_1, χ_2, ϕ_1 and ϕ_2, existence and uniqueness theorems are known [32, 268, 356, 398, 469]. Unfortunately too few of these theorems establish results in the large, which are known, in general, only for linear [356, 469] and for highly specialized nonlinear [268, 356] equations of type (7. 1). And because no general analytical technique is available to solve the initial-boundary value problem (7. 1) - (7. 5), attention will be directed to a numerical method for approximating a solution.

7. 3. Difference Approximations. In this section we will construct some useful difference approximations which, again, will render certain associated matrices mildly (diagonally) dominant.

Consider the wave operator

$$(7.6) \qquad L[u] \equiv u_{xx} - u_{tt} .$$

For $h > 0$, let the points (x,t), $(x,t+h)$, $(x,t-h)$, $(x,t-2h)$, $(x-h,t)$, $(x+h,t)$ be denoted, respectively, by $0,1,2,3,4,5$, as shown in Figure 7. 1. Let us seek to determine $\alpha_0, \alpha_1, \alpha_2, \alpha_3, \alpha_4, \alpha_5$ such that at (x,t)

$$u_{xx} - u_{tt} \equiv \sum_{i=0}^{5} \alpha_i u_i \ . \tag{7.7}$$

For this purpose, assume that u at each of the points numbered 1, 2, 3, 4, 5 in Figure 7.1 can be developed in a Taylor expansion about the point numbered 0. Then consider

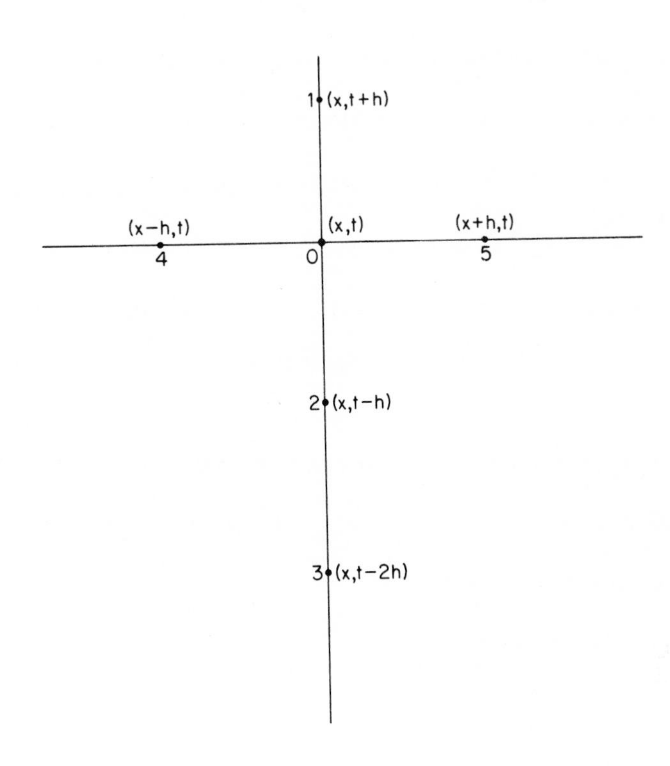

Figure 7.1

$$(u_{xx} - u_{tt})\big|_0 \equiv \sum_{i=0}^{5} \alpha_i u_i$$

$$\equiv (\alpha_0 + \alpha_1 + \alpha_2 + \alpha_3 + \alpha_4 + \alpha_5) u_0$$

$$+ (-h\alpha_4 + h\alpha_5) u_x\big|_0$$

$$+ (h\alpha_1 - h\alpha_2 - 2h\alpha_3) u_t\big|_0$$

$$+ (\frac{h^2}{2}\alpha_4 + \frac{h^2}{2}\alpha_5) u_{xx}\big|_0$$

$$+ (\frac{h^2}{2}\alpha_1 + \frac{h^2}{2}\alpha_2 + 2h^2\alpha_3) u_{tt}\big|_0$$

$$+ \sum_{1}^{5} (\alpha_i h^3) \; .$$

Setting

$$\begin{aligned}
\alpha_0 + \alpha_1 + \alpha_2 + \alpha_3 + \alpha_4 + \alpha_5 &= 0 \\
-\alpha_4 + \alpha_5 &= 0 \\
\alpha_1 - \alpha_2 - 2\alpha_3 &= 0 \\
\alpha_4 + \alpha_5 &= \frac{2}{h^2} \\
\alpha_1 + \alpha_2 + 4\alpha_3 &= -\frac{2}{h^2} \quad ,
\end{aligned}$$

then implies that

$$(7.8) \qquad \alpha_1 = -\frac{1}{h^2} - \frac{\alpha_0}{3}, \quad \alpha_2 = -\frac{1}{h^2} - \alpha_0, \quad \alpha_3 = \frac{\alpha_0}{3}, \quad \alpha_4 = \alpha_5 = \frac{1}{h^2} \; .$$

Thus, (7.7) takes the form

$$(7.9) \qquad u_{xx} - u_{tt} \equiv \alpha_0 u_0 + (-\frac{1}{h^2} - \frac{\alpha_0}{3}) u_1 + (-\frac{1}{h^2} - \alpha_0) u_2$$

$$+ (\frac{\alpha_0}{3}) u_3 + \frac{1}{h^2} u_4 + \frac{1}{h^2} u_5 + O(\alpha_0 h^3) \; .$$

For any choice of α_0 of the form $\alpha_0 = O(\frac{1}{h^2})$, the difference operator

$$(7.10)\qquad L_h[u] = \alpha_0 u_0 + (-\frac{1}{h^2} - \frac{\alpha_0}{3})u_1 + (-\frac{1}{h^2} - \alpha_0)u_2 + (\frac{\alpha_0}{3})u_3 + \frac{1}{h^2}u_4 + \frac{1}{h^2}u_5$$

will be called an approximation at (x, t) of the differential operator

$$(7.11)\qquad L[u] = u_{xx} - u_{tt}.$$

Next, recall that if the three points (x, t), $(x, t+h)$, and $(x, t+2h)$ are denoted, respectively, by $0, 1$ and 2, as shown in Figure 7.2, then a well known difference approximation for $\frac{\partial u}{\partial t}$ at the point numbered 0 is given by

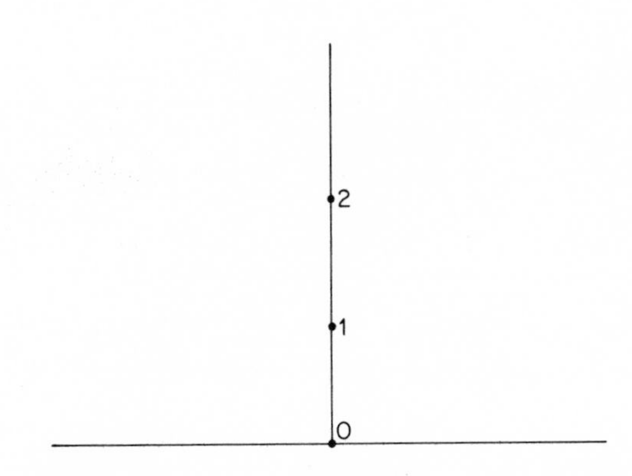

Figure 7.2

(7.12) $$\left.\frac{\partial u}{\partial t}\right|_0 = \frac{1}{2h}(-3u_0 + 4u_1 - u_2).$$

Finally, note that in practice we will attempt to choose α_0 so that in (7.10)

(7.13) $$|\alpha_0| > |\alpha_i|, \quad i = 1, 2, 3, 4, 5.$$

When these inequalities are valid, (7.10) is said to be mildly dominant. It is interesting to observe also that if $\alpha_3 = 0$, thus restricting (7.10) to the usual five point pattern, then no dominant difference operator can be constructed.

7.4. A Numerical Method. A numerical method for approximating a solution of initial-boundary value problem (7.1) - (7.5) proceeds as follows. Illustrative examples will be presented after the method is described in complete generality.

For two fixed positive integers n and N, let $h = \frac{a}{n}$ and let T be the set of points (x, Nh), where $0 \leq x \leq a$. Let S_1 be the set of points $(0, y)$ for which $0 \leq y \leq Nh$ and let S_2 be the set of points (a, y) for which $0 \leq y \leq Nh$. Finally set $S = I + T + S_1 + S_2$ (see Figure 6.2) and let R^* be the interior of S.

With $(0, 0)$ in S_h, for the above value of h construct and number in the usual way the interior lattice points R_h^* and the boundary lattice points S_h. Approximate u on T by means of an asymptotic estimate or by some periodicity property possessed by u. Then:

a) for each grid point in R_h^* whose coordinates are of the form (x, h), rite down the normal derivative approximation (7.12) at the point $(x, 0)$, hile

b) at each grid point in R_h^* whose coordinates are of the form (x, rh), $< r < N$, select an α_0, select respective difference approximations $u_{x,i}$ nd $u_{t,i}$ for u_x and u_t and write down the difference equation

7.14) $$\alpha_0 u_0 + \left(-\frac{1}{h^2} - \frac{\alpha_0}{3}\right)u_1 + \left(-\frac{1}{h^2} - \alpha_0\right)u_2 + \left(\frac{\alpha_0}{3}\right)u_3 + \frac{1}{h^2}u_4 + \frac{1}{h^2}u_5$$
$$= f(x, y, u_0, u_{x,i}, u_{t,i}).$$

ompletion of steps (a) and (b) and insertion of the known values of u on S ill then yield, say, k equations in $u_1, u_2, \ldots, u_k$, the solution of which onstitutes the numerical solution.

xample 1. If $a = 1$, consider the initial-boundary value problem defined by

7.15) $$u_{xx} - u_{tt} - u_t = 0$$

7.16) $$u(x, 0) = x$$

7.17) $$u_t(x, 0) = -x$$

7.18) $$u(0, t) = 0$$

7.19) $$u(1, t) = e^{-t}.$$

We seek a solution of (7.15) - (7.19) which, for all $x \in (0,1)$, satisfies

7.20) $$\lim_{t \to \infty} u(x, t) = 0.$$

For sufficient conditions to ensure such an asymptotic behavior consult, e.g., [469,482]. Also note that, as in the parabolic case (see (6.16) - 6.18)) asymptotic estimates can often be obtained easily from the knowledge of the existence of a steady-state solution.

Let us select $h = \frac{1}{3}$, $Nh = 2$. Then the ten resulting grid points in R are numbered $1, 2, \ldots, 10$, as shown in Figure 6.3.

From (7.16), (7.18) and (7.19) one has first that

$$
\begin{aligned}
&u(0,2) = 0 \qquad && u(0,\tfrac{1}{3}) = 0 \qquad && u(1,\tfrac{2}{3}) = e^{-2/3} \\
&u(0,\tfrac{5}{3}) = 0 && u(0,0) = 0 && u(1,1) = e^{-1} \\
&u(0,\tfrac{4}{3}) = 0 && u(\tfrac{1}{3},0) = \tfrac{1}{3} && u(1,\tfrac{4}{3}) = e^{-4/3} \\
&u(0,1) = 0 && u(\tfrac{2}{3},0) = \tfrac{2}{3} && u(1,\tfrac{5}{3}) = e^{-5/3} \\
&u(0,\tfrac{2}{3}) = 0 && u(1,0) = 1 && u(1,2) = e^{-2} \\
& && u(1,\tfrac{1}{3}) = e^{-1/3} &&
\end{aligned}
\tag{7.21}
$$

And, from (7.20), one approximates u on the line $t = 2$ by

$$u(x,2) = 0, \qquad 0 < x < 1. \tag{7.22}$$

Next, we associate with the point numbered 1 the equation

$$\frac{3}{2}[-3(\tfrac{1}{3}) + 4u_1 - u_3] = -\frac{1}{3} \tag{7.23}$$

which is merely the normal derivative approximation (7.12) applied at the point $(\frac{1}{3}, 0)$. Equation (7.23) is of course equivalent to

$$4u_1 - u_3 = \frac{7}{9}. \tag{7.24}$$

a completely analogous fashion, one associates with the point numbered 2 Figure 6. 3 the equation

$$4u_2 - u_4 = \frac{14}{9}. \tag{7.25}$$

Next observe that if, in the notation of Figure 7. 1, one sets $\alpha_0 = -\frac{4}{h^2}$ nd $u_t|_0 = \frac{u_0 - u_2}{h}$, then (7. 9) implies that differential equation (7. 15) can e approximated by the difference equation

$$-\frac{4}{h^2}u_0 + (\frac{1}{3h^2})u_1 + (\frac{3}{h^2})u_2 - \frac{4}{3h^2}u_3 + \frac{1}{h^2}u_4 + \frac{1}{h^2}u_5 - (\frac{u_0 - u_2}{h}) = 0 . \tag{7.26}$$

or $h = \frac{1}{3}$, this mildly dominant approximation is equivalent to

$$-13u_0 + u_1 + 10u_2 - 4u_3 + 3u_4 + 3u_5 = 0 , \tag{7.27}$$

hich, when applied consecutively at the points $3, 4, \ldots, 10$ in Figure 6. 3, ields with the aid of (7. 21) and (7. 22) the algebraic system

$$10u_1 - 13u_3 + 3u_4 + u_5 = \frac{4}{3} \tag{7.28}$$

$$10u_2 + 3u_3 - 13u_4 + u_6 = \frac{8}{3} - 3e^{-2/3} \tag{7.29}$$

$$-4u_1 + 10u_3 - 13u_5 + 3u_6 + u_7 = 0 \tag{7.30}$$

$$-4u_2 + 10u_4 + 3u_5 - 13u_6 + u_8 = -3e^{-1} \tag{7.31}$$

$$-4u_3 + 10u_5 - 13u_7 + 3u_8 + u_9 = 0 \tag{7.32}$$

$$-4u_4 + 10u_6 + 3u_7 - 13u_8 + u_{10} = -3e^{-4/3} \tag{7.33}$$

$$-4u_5 + 10u_7 - 13u_9 + 3u_{10} = 0 \tag{7.34}$$

$$-4u_6 + 10u_8 + 3u_9 - 13u_{10} = -3e^{-5/3} . \tag{7.35}$$

The solution of system (7. 24), (7. 25), (7. 27) - (7. 35) was found easily by the generalized Newton's method and differed from the exact solution $u = xe^{-t}$ of (7.15) - (7.19) at each point by at most 0.01.

Example 2. The problem (7.15) - (7.19) was considered again. This time, however, we set $Nh = 10$, $h = 0.1$, $u(x, 10) = 0$. Using (7.26) again, the steps analogous to those described in Example 1 yielded 891 linear algebraic equations in 891 unknowns. Their solution was found on the CDC 3600 by the generalized Newton's method with zero initial vector and $w = 1.3$. The running time was 35 seconds. The numerical results agreed with the exact solution usually to 5 decimal places. The maximum error was $4 \cdot 10^{-3}$ and occurred at the point (0.5, 0.9). The minimum error was $6 \cdot 10^{-9}$ and occurred at the point (0.1, 6.5).

Example 3. For $a = 1$, consider the initial-boundary value problem defined by

$$u_{xx} - u_{tt} = 2(t-x)(t+x+2)u^3 \tag{7.36}$$

$$u(x, 0) = (1+x)^{-1} \tag{7.37}$$

$$u_t(x, 0) = -(1+x)^{-1} \tag{7.38}$$

$$u(0, t) = (1+t)^{-1} \tag{7.39}$$

$$u(1, t) = \frac{1}{2}(1+t)^{-1} . \tag{7.40}$$

We seek a solution of (7.36) - (7.40) which, for all $x \in [0,1]$, satisfies

$$\lim_{t \to \infty} u(x, t) = 0 . \tag{7.41}$$

We set $Nh = 200$ and approximated (7.36) by

(7.42)
$$-\frac{4}{h^2}u_0 + \left(\frac{1}{3h^2}\right)u_1 + \left(\frac{3}{h^2}\right)u_2 - \frac{4}{3h^2}u_3 + \frac{1}{h^2}u_4 + \frac{1}{h^2}u_5 = 2(t-x)(t+x+2)u_0^3 .$$

By setting $h = \frac{1}{5}$ and proceeding in a fashion analogous to that in Example 1, the resulting system of 3996 nonlinear algebraic equations was solved by the generalized Newton's method with zero initial vector and $w = 1$. The numerical results agreed with the exact solution $u = (1+x)^{-1}(1+t)^{-1}$ usually to five, but to at least two, decimal places. The running time was three minutes and forty four seconds.

Finally, it should be noted that research to develop the mathematical basis for the method of this lecture is at present in progress.

Lecture 8 - Approximate Extremization of Functionals

8.1 Introduction. Historically, one of the oldest mathematical disciplines to be intimately involved with applied problems is the calculus of variations. And in developing numerical methods for nonlinear problems in which the defining equation may be more than mildly nonlinear, we shall examine first the classical variational problems in one and two dimensions.

The fundamental problem in the calculus of variations may be formulated as follows. For a, b, α, and β real numbers, with $a < b$, and for given $F(x, y, p)$ which has continuous first order partial derivatives, find a function $y(x)$ which is defined and has continuous first derivatives for $a \le x \le b$, which satisfies the boundary conditions

$$y(a) = \alpha, \quad y(b) = \beta, \tag{8.1}$$

and which minimizes (or maximizes) the integral

$$J = \int_a^b F(x, y, y')dx \; . \tag{8.2}$$

Geometrically, as shown in Figure 8.1, the fundamental problem in the calculus of variations requires that, out of all the continuously differentiable functions defined on $a \le x \le b$, whose graphs pass through the two points (a, α) and (b, β), one must find a function $y(x)$ which minimizes the given integral (8.2).

Because the value of (8.2) depends on a function, and not just on a

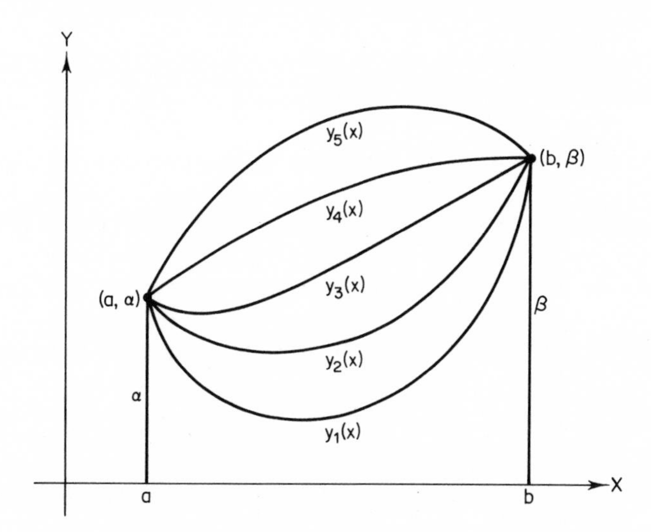

Figure 8.1

real number, the integral (8. 2) is in reality a function of a function and therefore is called a <u>functional</u>.

<u>Example</u>. Suppose one is given the functional

$$J = \int_0^1 (x^2 y - y')dx \tag{8. 3}$$

and $a = 0$, $b = 1$, $\alpha = 1$, $\beta = 0$. Then, examples of continuously differentiable functions which satisfy the boundary conditions

$$y(0) = 1, \quad y(1) = 0 \tag{8. 4}$$

are

$$y = 1 - x$$

$$y = 1 - x^3$$

$$y = x^2 - 2x + 1,$$

which, when inserted into functional (8. 3) yield

$$J(1-x) = \int_0^1 [x^2(1-x) - (-1)]\,dx = \frac{13}{12}$$

$$J(1-x^3) = \int_0^1 [x^2(1-x^3) - (-3x^2)]\,dx = \frac{7}{6}$$

$$J(x^2-2x+1) = \int_0^1 [x^2(x^2-2x+1) - (2x-2)]\,dx = \frac{31}{30}$$

The problem of finding $y(x)$ which is continuously differentiable on $0 \leq x \leq 1$, which satisfies (8. 4), and which minimizes (8. 3) is a fundamental type problem of the calculus of variations.

Now, analytically, the fundamental problem in the calculus of variations is, in general, exceptionally difficult to solve. As in the elementary calculus, where one attempts to find a minimum of a function

$$y = f(x) \tag{8. 5}$$

by solving the equation

$$f'(x) = 0, \tag{8. 6}$$

so in the calculus of variations one can attempt to find a minimum of a functional

$$J = \int_a^b F(x, y, y')dx \tag{8. 7}$$

by solving the equation

(8. 8)
$$\frac{\partial F}{\partial y} - \frac{d}{dx}\frac{\partial F}{\partial y'} = 0,$$

which results by setting what is known as the Frechet derivative of functional (8. 7) equal to zero. The equation (8. 8) is known as the Euler differential equation and a great portion of the calculus of variations is devoted to the study of the problem defined by (8. 1) and (8. 8) rather than to the problem defined by (8. 1) and (8. 2).

Example. The Euler equation of the functional

$$\int_0^1 [xy^3 - (y')^2 + 3xyy']\, dx$$

is

$$(3xy^2 + 3xy') - \frac{d}{dx}(-2y' + 3xy) = 0$$

or, equivalently,

$$2y'' - 3y + 3xy^2 = 0$$

Euler differential equation (8. 8) is, in general, a nonlinear, second order, ordinary differential equation. And although such equations are, in general, very difficult to solve, still they seem to be more accessible analytically than the functionals from which they are derived. Nevertheless, numerically it appears to be much easier to solve the original fundamental problem of the calculus of variations than to solve the one defined by (8. 1) and (8. 8), and so the approach here will be to examine problems in the literature which are usually stated in terms of (8. 1) and (8. 8) by returning to their original variational formulation in terms of (8. 1) and (8. 2), and by then applying a rather simple numerical technique. Such an approach is also motivated by the observations that for most applied problems one cannot solve the associated Euler differential equation analytically and that just as a solution of (8. 6) yields only an extremal of (8. 5), so a solution of (8. 8) need not yield a minimum (or maximum) of (8. 7).

8. 2. A Numerical Method. Consider now the fundamental problem of the calculus of variations, that is, the boundary value problem defined by (8. 1) and (8. 2). Divide the interval $a \le x \le b$ into n equal parts, each of length $h = \frac{b-a}{n}$, by the points $a = x_0 < x_1 < x_2 < \dots < x_{n-1} < x_n = b$ (see Figure 8. 2). Thus, $h = x_i - x_{i-1}$ for $i = 1, 2, \dots, n$. Let $y_i = y(x_i)$ for $i = 0, 1, \dots, n$. Then approximate the functional

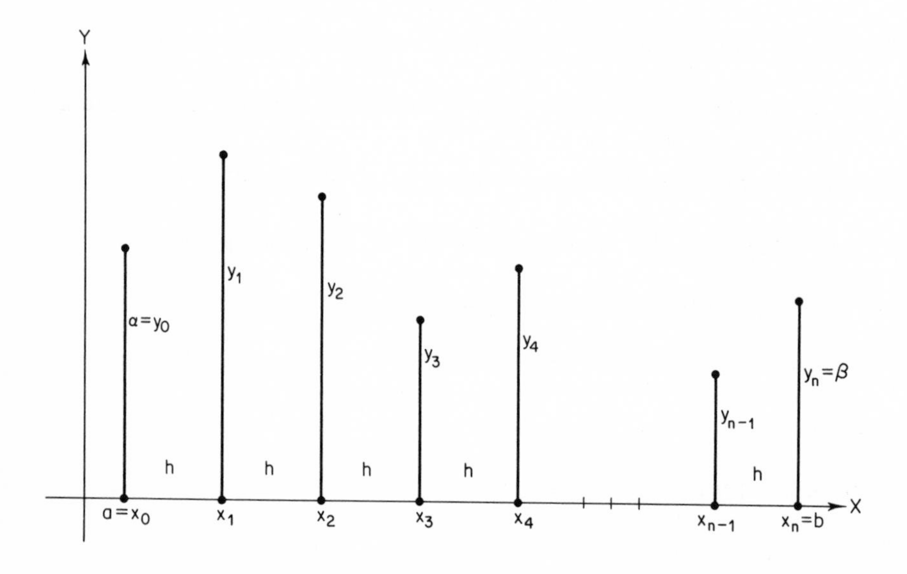

Figure 8.2

$$J = \int_a^b F(x, y, y')dx \tag{8.9}$$

y the function

$$J_n = h \sum_{i=1}^{n} F(x_{i-1}, y_{i-1}, \frac{y_i - y_{i-1}}{h}). \tag{8.10}$$

ince, by (8.1), $y_0 = \alpha$ and $y_n = \beta$, it follows that J_n is a function only f $y_1, y_2, \ldots, y_{n-1}$. To find an extremal of J_n, then, consider the system f equations

$$\frac{\partial J_n}{\partial y_i} = 0; \quad i = 1, 2, \ldots, n-1 . \tag{8.11}$$

solution of (8.11) will constitute an approximation at $x_1, x_2, \ldots, x_{n-1}$ f a function $y(x)$ which is a solution of the fundamental problem of the alculus of variations.

The function (8.10) is obtained by a simple rectangular integration pproximation of (8.9) in which derivatives are replaced by forward differences.

xample. Let S be the unit sphere, whose equation is $x^2+y^2+z^2 = 1$. onsider the problem of finding the shortest path on S between $(1, 0, 0)$ nd $(\frac{\sqrt{2}}{2}, 0, \frac{\sqrt{2}}{2})$. For this purpose let S be parametrized by

$$\begin{aligned} x &= \cos \phi \cos \theta \\ y &= \cos \phi \sin \theta \\ z &= \sin \phi \end{aligned} \tag{8.12}$$

here ϕ represents latitude and θ represents longitude, as shown in

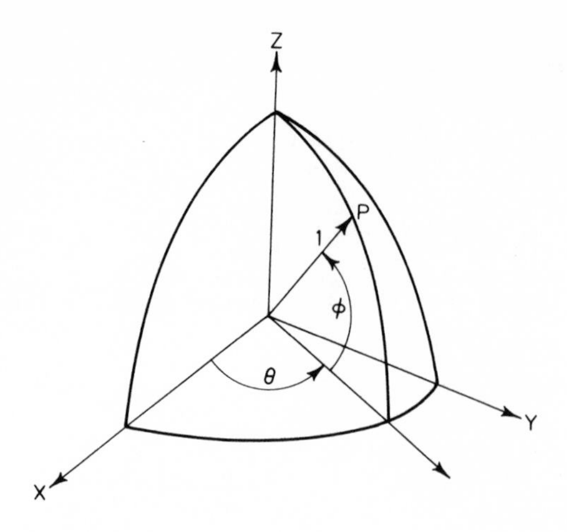

Figure 8.3

Figure 8. 3. Then S can be given vectorially by

(8. 13) $$\vec{x} = (\cos\phi\cos\theta,\ \cos\phi\sin\theta,\ \sin\phi)$$

and

$$E \equiv \frac{\partial\vec{x}}{\partial\phi}\cdot\frac{\partial\vec{x}}{\partial\phi} = 1$$

$$F \equiv \frac{\partial\vec{x}}{\partial\phi}\cdot\frac{\partial\vec{x}}{\partial\theta} = 0$$

$$G \equiv \frac{\partial\vec{x}}{\partial\theta}\cdot\frac{\partial\vec{x}}{\partial\theta} = \cos^2\phi\ .$$

Since [412] geodesics are extrema of the functional

$$\int_{\phi_1}^{\phi_2} \sqrt{(E + F\frac{d\theta}{d\phi} + G(\frac{d\theta}{d\phi})^2)}\,d\phi, \qquad \theta = \theta(\phi)\ ,$$

it follows that we wish to extremize the functional

(8. 14) $$J = \int_0^{\pi/4} \sqrt{[1 + (\cos^2\phi)(\frac{d\theta}{d\phi})^2]}\,d\phi$$

subject to the boundary conditions

$$\theta(0) = \theta(\tfrac{\pi}{4}) = 0. \tag{8.15}$$

Setting $h = \pi/16$ implies $\phi_0 = 0$, $\phi_1 = \pi/16$, $\phi_2 = \pi/8$, $\phi_3 = 3\pi/16$, $\phi_4 = \pi/4$ and $\theta(\phi_i) = \theta_i$, $\theta_0 = \theta_4 = 0$. Functional (8.14) is then approximated by the function

$$J_4 = \frac{\pi}{16}\sum_{i=1}^{4}\{\sqrt{[1 + (\cos^2\phi_{i-1})(\frac{\theta_i-\theta_{i-1}}{\pi/16})^2]}\} \tag{8.16}$$

and system (8.11) takes the form of the following three equations in $\theta_1, \theta_2, \theta_3$:

$$\frac{\theta_1}{\sqrt{[1+(\frac{\theta_1}{\pi/16})^2]}} - \frac{(\cos^2\frac{\pi}{16})(\theta_2-\theta_1)}{\sqrt{[1+(\cos^2\frac{\pi}{16})(\frac{\theta_2-\theta_1}{\pi/16})^2]}} = 0$$

$$\frac{(\cos^2\frac{\pi}{16})(\theta_2-\theta_1)}{\sqrt{[1+(\cos^2\frac{\pi}{16})(\frac{\theta_2-\theta_1}{\pi/16})^2]}} - \frac{(\cos^2\frac{\pi}{8})(\theta_3-\theta_2)}{\sqrt{[1+(\cos^2\frac{\pi}{8})(\frac{\theta_3-\theta_2}{\pi/16})^2]}} = 0$$

$$\frac{(\cos^2\frac{\pi}{8})(\theta_3-\theta_2)}{\sqrt{[1+(\cos^2\frac{\pi}{8})(\frac{\theta_3-\theta_2}{\pi/16})^2]}} - \frac{(\cos^2\frac{3\pi}{16})\theta_3}{\sqrt{[1+(\cos^2\frac{3\pi}{16})(\frac{\theta_3}{\pi/16})^2]}} = 0 .$$

The generalized Newton's method with initial guess $\theta_1 = \frac{1}{2}$, $\theta_2 = 1$, $\theta_3 = \frac{1}{2}$ and with $w = 1.8$ was applied to solve the above nonlinear algebraic system. On the CDC 3600 the number of iterations was 95 and the running time was 8 sec. The answers were $\theta_1 = \theta_2 = \theta_3 = 0 \cdot 10^{-12} = 0$ so that from (8.12) one has

$$(x_1, y_1, z_1) = (\cos\phi_1 \cos\theta_1, \cos\phi_1 \sin\theta_1, \sin\phi_1) = (\cos\frac{\pi}{16}, 0, \sin\frac{\pi}{16})$$

$$(x_2, y_2, z_2) = (\cos\phi_2 \cos\theta_2, \cos\phi_2 \sin\theta_2, \sin\phi_2) = (\cos\frac{\pi}{8}, 0, \sin\frac{\pi}{8})$$

$$(x_3, y_3, z_3) = (\cos\phi_3 \cos\theta_3, \cos\phi_3 \sin\theta_3, \sin\phi_3) = (\cos\frac{3\pi}{16}, 0, \sin\frac{3\pi}{16}).$$

Since the shortest path sought is completely determined analytically by $\theta = 0$, $0 \le \phi \le (\pi/4)$, the unusual result follows that the above three points actually lie on the resulting geodesic.

For details of examples in which system (8.11) consists of as many as 1500 equations, and for the existing mathematical theory supporting the method of this lecture, see [172] and [174].

8.3. Free Boundary Value Problems. All the ideas and theory presented thus far extend in a natural way to integration formulae other than that incorporated in (8.10) and to free boundary value problems. We shall illustrate both of these possibilities by means of the following treatment of a control theory problem.

Consider the problem of minimizing the functional

$$J = \int_0^1 [y^2 + (y')^2]\, dx \tag{8.17}$$

subject to the boundary conditions

$$y(0) = 1, \quad y'(1) = 0. \tag{8.18}$$

Setting $h_i \equiv 0.25$ implies $x_0 = 0$, $x_1 = 0.25$, $x_2 = 0.5$, $x_3 = 0.75$, $x_4 = 1$. Functional (8.17) then can be approximated by the following trapezoidal integration formula:

$$J \sim \frac{1}{8}[y_0^2+(y_0')^2+2y_1^2+2(y_1')^2+2y_2^2+2(y_2')^2+2y_3^2+2(y_3')^2+y_4^2+(y_4')^2]$$

which, after the insertion of (8.18), reduces to

$$J \sim \frac{1}{8}[1+(y_0')^2+2y_1^2+2(y_1')^2+2y_2^2+2(y_2')^2+2y_3^2+2(y_3')^2+y_4^2] \tag{8.19}$$

Next, inserting into (8.19) a forward difference approximation for y_0' and central difference approximations for y_1', y_2' and y_3', one has

$$J \sim J_4 = \frac{1}{8}[1+(\frac{y_1-1}{0.25})^2 + 2y_1^2 + 2(\frac{y_2-1}{0.5})^2$$

$$+ 2y_2^2 + 2(\frac{y_3-y_1}{0.5})^2 + 2y_3^2 + 2(\frac{y_4-y_2}{0.5})^2 + y_4^2].$$

In order to minimize J_4, consider the equations:

$$\frac{\partial J_4}{\partial y_i} = 0, \qquad i = 1, 2, 3, 4,$$

which, in this case, are equivalent to

$$13y_1 - 4y_3 = 8$$

$$9y_2 - 4y_4 = 4$$

$$4y_1 - 5y_3 = 0$$

$$8y_2 - 9y_4 = 0$$

The solution of this linear algebraic system is then $Y_1 = \frac{40}{49} \sim 0.816$, $Y_2 = \frac{36}{49} \sim 0.735$, $Y_3 = \frac{32}{49} \sim 0.653$, $Y_4 = \frac{32}{49} \sim 0.653$, which compares favorably with the exact solution $y_1 = 0.839$, $y_2 = 0.731$, $y_3 = 0.668$, $y_4 = 0.648$, determined from the exact solution

$$y(x) = \frac{\cosh(1 - x)}{\cosh 1}$$

8.4. Variational Problems and Partial Differential Equations. As regards partial differential equations, the fundamental problem of the calculus of variations can be formulated as follows. Let $F(x, y, u, p, q)$ be continuous in each of its variables. Let R be a simply connected, bounded region R whose boundary S is piecewise regular. Finally, let $f(x, y)$ be defined and continuous on S. Then one must find a function $u(x, y)$ which has continuous first partial derivatives on $R + S$, satisfies

$$u \equiv \phi \quad \text{on} \quad S \tag{8.20}$$

and minimizes (or maximizes)

$$J = \iint_{R+S} F(x, y, u, u_x, u_y)\,dA. \tag{8.21}$$

The Euler differential equation of (8.21) is

$$F_u - \frac{\partial}{\partial x} F_{u_x} - \frac{\partial}{\partial y} F_{u_y} = 0 \tag{8.22}$$

Example 1. The Euler equation of the functional

$$J = \iint_{R+S} [u_x^2 + u_y^2 + 2e^u - 2]\,dA$$

is

$$u_{xx} + u_{yy} = e^u.$$

Example 2. The Euler equation of the functional

$$J = \iint_{R+S} [u_x^2 + u_y^2 + \frac{2u^3}{3} - \frac{2}{3}] \, dA$$

is

$$u_{xx} + u_{yy} = u^2$$

We shall next study Dirichlet problems defined by (8. 20) and (8. 22) by applying to (8. 20) and (8. 21) a direct generalization of the method developed in Section 8. 2.

Lecture 9 - Nonlinear Problems

9.1. Introduction. Dirichlet problems for the equations

$$\Delta u = e^u \tag{9.1}$$

$$\Delta u = u^2 \tag{9.2}$$

and, in general, for

$$\Delta u = G(u), \tag{9.3}$$

often originate in fact in a variational form, for (9.3) is the Euler equation of the functional

$$J = \iint_{R+S} [u_x^2 + u_y^2 + 2 \int_0^u G(t)dt]\, dA \tag{9.4}$$

But since we have already developed efficient methods for dealing directly with mildly nonlinear equations (9.1) and (9.2), we shall turn to Dirichlet problems for which the given elliptic equation is more complicated than (9.3) and usually cannot be handled easily, if at all, by the methods described in Lecture 5.

9.2. The Plateau Problem. Let R be a simply connected, bounded region whose boundary S is piecewise regular. Let $f(x, y)$ be defined and continuous on S. Then the Dirichlet problem of finding $u(x, y)$ which is continuous on $R + S$, satisfies

$$u = f \text{ on } S \tag{9.5}$$

and satisfies the nonlinear elliptic differential equation

$$(9.6) \qquad (1+u_y^2)u_{xx} - 2u_x u_y u_{xy} + (1+u_x^2)u_{yy} = 0$$

on R will be called the Plateau problem.

The Plateau problem is intimately related with the physical problem of soap films, that is, of the determining the shape of a soap film which results after having dipped a closed, three dimensional wire into a soap solution [357]. Indeed, (9.6) is the Euler equation of the integral which defines the surface area of the resulting soap film, that is, of

$$(9.7) \qquad J = \iint_{R+S} \sqrt{1+u_x^2+u_y^2}\, dA\ .$$

In elasticity problems, like those for soap films, one wishes to minimize (9.7).

Rather than discuss the extensive details of an abstract extension of the numerical method of Lecture 8 to general problems in partial differential equations, we shall show very simply how to treat these by means of the following illustrative Plateau problem. More complicated problems can be treated similarly.

Example. Let S be the square whose vertices are (0, 0), (1, 0), (1, 1) and (0, 1). Let R be the interior of S. On S define $f(x, y)$ by

$$(9.8) \qquad f(x,y) = x - 3y$$

and consider the associated Plateau problem.

Our numerical approach will center about minimizing functional (9.7) subject to the restriction (9.8). For this purpose, take $h = \frac{1}{3}$ and construct

R_h and S_h. It will be convenient, however, in the present discussion to also allow the vertices (0, 0), (1, 0), (1, 1) and (0, 1) to be points of S_h, and this will be done. Number the points of R_h with 1, 2, 3, 4 and those of S_h with 5, 6, 7, 8, 9, 10, ..., 16, as shown in Figure 9.1. Next triangulate, in

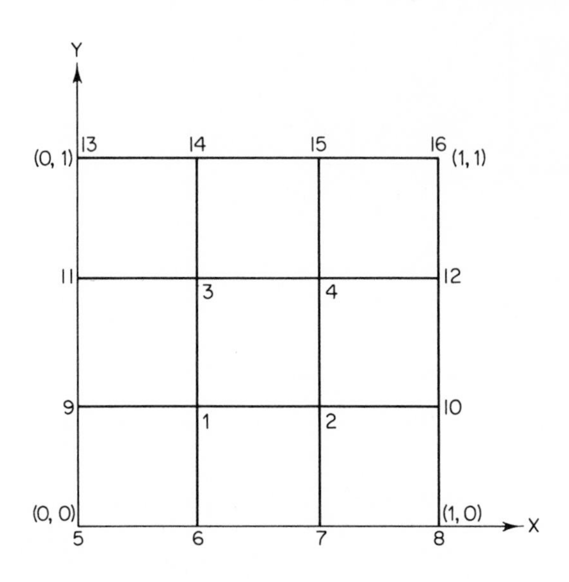

Figure 9.1

any fashion, each subsquare shown in Figure 9.1, so that $R + S$ is thereby divided into 18 mutually disjoint subtriangular regions, a possible arrangement of which is shown in Figure 9.2. Notice that the process of triangularization introduces no new points into R_h and S_h. Number these triangular regions $R_1, R_2, \ldots, R_{18}$, in any order, and let the boundary of each R_i be denoted by S_i, $i = 1, 2, \ldots, 18$.

Now, note that (9.7) can be rewritten in the form

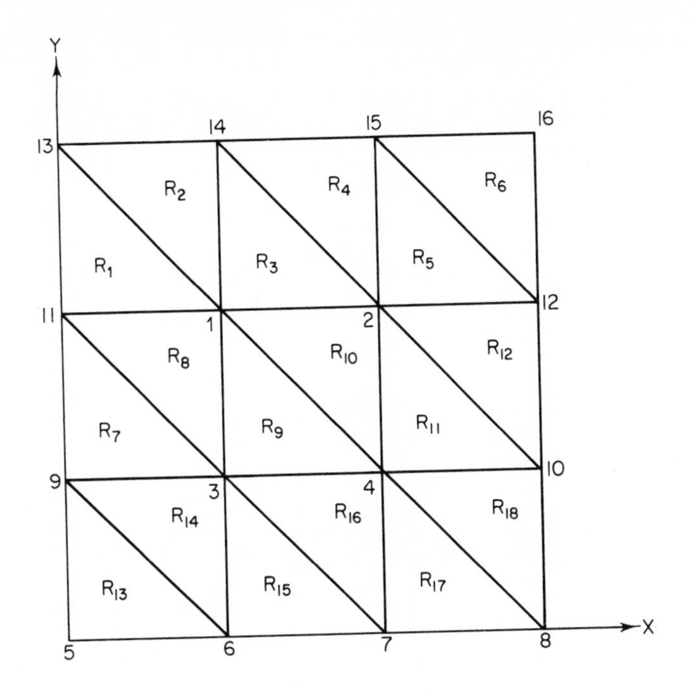

Figure 9.2

$$
\begin{aligned}
J &= \iint_{R+S} \sqrt{1+u_x^2+u_y^2}\; dA \\
&= \sum_{i=1}^{18} \iint_{R_i+S_i} \sqrt{1+u_x^2+u_y^2}\; dA \\
&= \iint_{R_1+S_1} \sqrt{1+u_x^2+u_y^2}\; dA + \iint_{R_2+S_2} \sqrt{1+u_x^2+u_y^2}\; dA + \ldots + \iint_{R_{18}+S_{18}} \sqrt{1+u_x^2+u_y^2}\; dA .
\end{aligned}
$$

Consider first,

$$
I_1 = \iint_{R_1+S_1} \sqrt{1+u_x^2+u_y^2}\; dA .
$$

In order to approximate I_1, fix the right angle vertex of S_1, which is the point numbered 11 in Figure 9. 2, and at it approximate u_x and u_y by using function values only at other points of S_1. Thus,

$$u_x\Big|_{11} \sim \frac{u_1 - u_{11}}{1/3}$$

$$u_y\Big|_{11} \sim \frac{u_{13} - u_{11}}{1/3} ,$$

which, from (9. 8), implies that

$$u_x\Big|_{11} \sim \frac{u_1 - (-2)}{1/3} = 3u_1 + 6$$

$$u_y\Big|_{11} \sim \frac{-3-(-2)}{1/3} = -3 .$$

Thus, I_1 can be approximated by

$$I_1^* = \frac{1}{18} \cdot \sqrt{1 + (3u_1+6)^2 + (-3)^2} .$$

Consider next

$$I_2 = \iint_{R_2+S_2} \sqrt{1+u_x^2+u_y^2}\, dA .$$

In order to approximate I_2, fix the right angle vextex of S_2, which is the point numbered 14 in Figure 9. 2, and at it approximate u_x and u_y by using function values only at other points of S_2. Thus

$$u_x\Big|_{14} \sim \frac{u_{14} - u_{13}}{1/3} = \frac{-\frac{8}{3} - (-3)}{1/3} = 1$$

$$u_y\Big|_{14} \sim \frac{u_{14} - u_1}{1/3} = \frac{-\frac{8}{3} - u_1}{1/3} = -8 - 3u_1$$

and as an approximation to I_2, take

$$I_2^* = \frac{1}{18} \cdot \sqrt{1 + (1)^2 + (-8 - 3u_1)^2}$$

One proceeds in the fashion indicated above until each integral

$$I_i = \iint_{R_i+S_i} \sqrt{1 + u_x^2 + u_y^2}\, dA, \qquad i = 1, 2, \ldots, 18$$

is approximated by an I_i^*, which is determined by rectangular integration. In each I_i^*, u_x and u_y are approximated at the right angle vertex of S_i by means of function values only at points of S_i.

One next approximates J by J_{18}, where

$$J_{18} = \sum_{i=1}^{18} I_i^*$$

which, for illustrative purposes, is now given in full detail:

$$\begin{aligned}
(9.9) \quad J_{18} = \frac{1}{18}[&\sqrt{10+(3u_1+6)^2} + \sqrt{2+(3u_1+8)^2} \\
&+ \sqrt{1+(3u_2-3u_1)^2 + (3u_1+8)^2} + \sqrt{2+(3u_2+7)^2} \\
&+ \sqrt{1+(3u_2+3)^2 + (3u_2+7)^2} + \sqrt{11} + \sqrt{10+(3u_3+3)^2} \\
&+ \sqrt{1+(3u_1+6)^2 + (3u_1-3u_3)^2} + \sqrt{1+(3u_4-3u_3)^2 + (3u_1-3u_3)^2} \\
&+ \sqrt{1+(3u_2-3u_1)^2+(3u_2-3u_4)^2} + \sqrt{1+9u_4^2 + (3u_2-3u_4)^2} \\
&+ \sqrt{10+(3u_2+3)^2} + \sqrt{11} + \sqrt{1+(3u_3+3)^2+(3u_3-1)^2} + \sqrt{2+(3u_3-1)^2} \\
&+ \sqrt{1+(3u_4-3u_3)^2 + (3u_4-2)^2} + \sqrt{2+(3u_4-2)^2} + \sqrt{10+9u_4^2}\ ]
\end{aligned}$$

Note immediately that J_{18} is a function only of u_1, u_2, u_3 and u_4, which are of course function values at the points of R_h. As an approximation of the minimum of J at the points of R_h, we take the minimum of J_{18} at the points of R_h, and we find these by solving the system

$$\frac{\partial J_{18}}{\partial u_i} = 0, \qquad i = 1, 2, 3, 4.$$

These can be found by the generalized Newton's method and in this case are

$$U_1 = -\frac{5}{3}, \quad U_2 = -\frac{4}{3}, \quad U_3 = -\frac{2}{3}, \quad U_4 = -\frac{1}{3},$$

which, interestingly enough, coincide with the exact values of the solution $u = x-3y$ of the given problem at the points of R_h

In a sense, the example given above was "rigged". Indeed, the solution

$$u = x - 3y$$

of the given Plateau problem graphs as a plane, and this solution is geometrically obvious once one looks at the boundary function. However, the example does serve to illustrate the numerical method, and with this in mind, we next apply the method to an interesting, but very difficult, problem in fluid dynamics.

9.3. A Subsonic Flow Problem. The study of fluid flow is, in general, divided into two parts, the study of liquids and the study of gases. For liquids it is assumed by many that compressibility is of no consequence but friction, or viscosity, is. For gases, it is assumed by many that compressibility is important but that viscosity is not. And of the large variety of mathematical models which are available we shall examine now the flow of a compressible inviscid gas. The model to be studied is that of von Mises [444] and has received much attention in the literature.

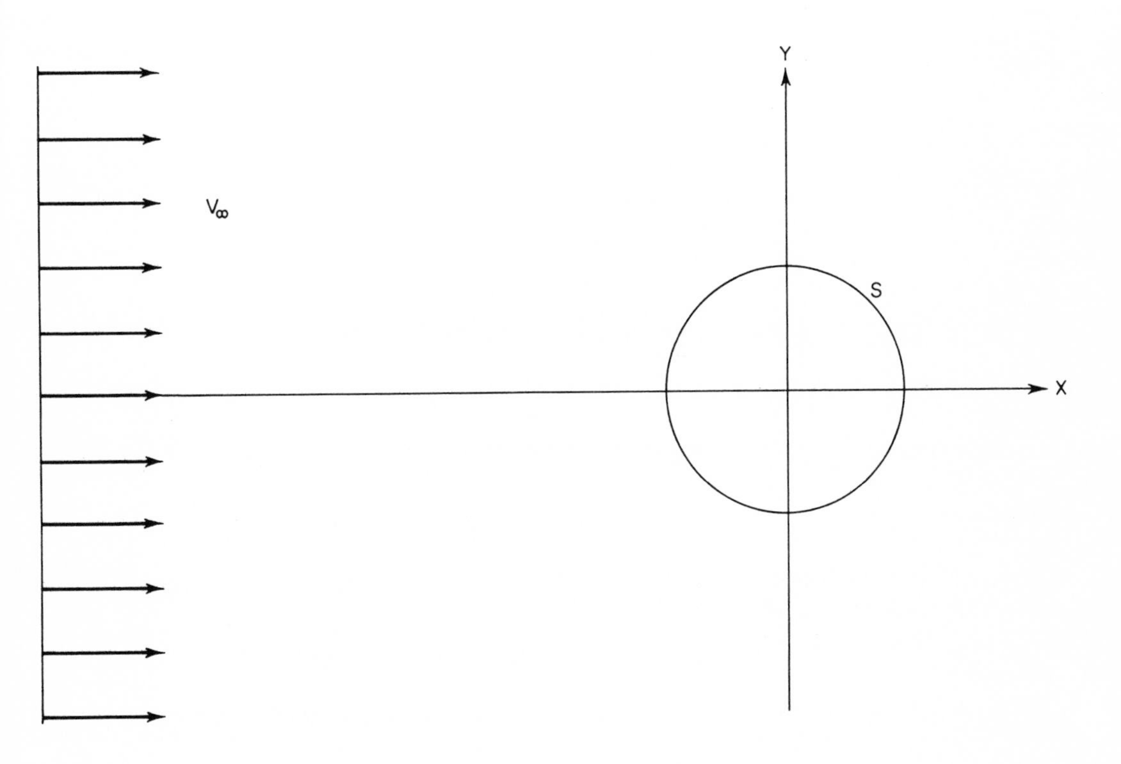

Figure 9.3

Consider a steady stream of air which begins at $x = -\infty$ with a velocity V_∞, which is parallel to the X axis, and which flows around an object S which is located at the origin of the XY system. The problem is to describe the flow of the air around the object S.

For simplicity we shall assume that S is a unit circle and that the flow is also irrotational (contains no rotational motions, and hence no vortices) and homentropic (the entropy is constant).

In terms of the quantities

ρ = density

p = pressure = $a\rho^{1.405}$, $\underline{a}$ a constant

V_∞ = positive constant

u_x = x component of velocity $\vec{v}$

u_y = y component of velocity $\vec{v}$

$c^2 = \dfrac{dp}{d\rho}$

M = Mach no. = $\left(\dfrac{u_x^2+u_y^2}{c^2}\right)^{1/2} = \left|\dfrac{V}{c}\right|$

R^* = exterior of S,

the boundary value problem which is usually studied is an exterior problem which can be formulated as follows. Find $u = u(x, y)$ which is continuous on $R^* \cup S$, which satisfies

$$(c^2-u_x^2)u_{xx} - 2u_x u_y u_{xy} + (c^2 - u_y^2)u_{yy} = 0 \quad \text{on} \quad R^*, \tag{9.10}$$

and which satisfies the boundary conditions

$$\frac{\partial u}{\partial n} = 0, \quad \text{on} \quad S \tag{9.11}$$

$$u_x = V_\infty, \quad \text{at} \quad x = -\infty \tag{9.12}$$

Equation (9.10) is elliptic, parabolic, or hyperbolic according as M is less than unity, equal to unity, or greater than unity. At a point where $M < 1$ the flow is called subsonic, where $M = 1$ it is called sonic, and where $M > 1$ it is called supersonic. And because in general when a flow is supersonic one usually does not want to exclude the possibility of vortices, we shall continue under the assumption that at each point of $R^* + S$ one has

$$(9.13) \qquad M < 1 .$$

For the flow defined by (9.10) - (9.13), Lush and Cherry [267] have shown that (9.10) is the Euler equation on R^* of the functional (in polar coordinates)

$$(9.14) \qquad J(u) = \int_0^{2\pi}\int_1^{\infty} p_{\infty}[F-1+(1.405)M_{\infty}^2 H]\, r\,dr\,d\theta ,$$

where

$$(9.15) \qquad u = Vx + V\Omega$$

$$(9.16) \qquad F = [1-\frac{0.405}{2}M_{\infty}^2\{2\cos\theta\frac{\partial\Omega}{\partial r} - \frac{2\sin\theta}{r}\frac{\partial\Omega}{\partial\theta} + (\frac{\partial\Omega}{\partial r})^2 + \frac{1}{r^2}(\frac{\partial\Omega}{\partial\theta})^2\}]^{1.405/0.405}$$

$$(9.17) \qquad H = (1-\frac{1}{r^2})(\frac{\partial\Omega}{\partial r})\cos\theta - (1+\frac{1}{r^2})(\frac{\partial\Omega}{\partial\theta})\frac{\sin\theta}{r} .$$

Moreover, Lush and Cherry showed that it is necessary to maximize J. The boundary conditions (9.11) and (9.12) in polars are

$$(9.18) \qquad \Omega = 0 \quad \text{at} \quad x = -\infty$$

$$(9.19) \qquad \frac{\partial\Omega}{\partial n} = -\cos\theta \quad \text{on} \quad S.$$

Now because it is known that the flow is symmetric about the X and the Y axes and because one expects S to have no effect on the flow at any large distance away from S, in place of maximizing (9.14), we shall attempt to maximize

$$J^*(u) = \int_{\frac{\pi}{2}}^{\pi} \int_{1}^{r^*} p_\infty [F - 1 + 1.405(M_\infty^2)H] \, r \, dr \, d\theta, \quad r^* >> 1 . \tag{9.20}$$

The region of integration of (9.20) in the XY plane, that is, in the physical plane, is shown in the shaded annular section of Figure 9.4. In the polar plane, however, this region is merely the shaded rectangular region

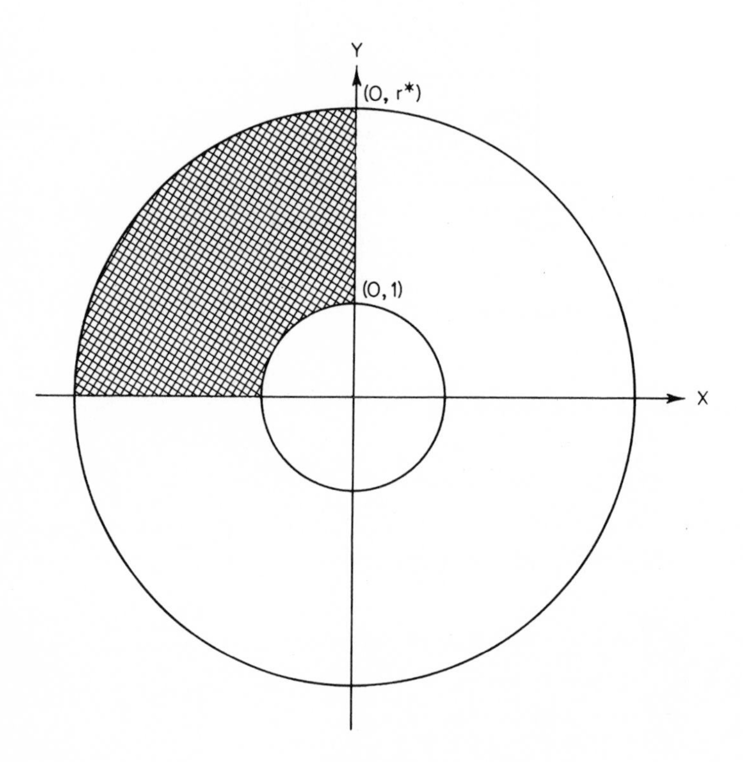

Figure 9.4

shown in Figure 9. 5. Thus, we wish to maximize (9. 20) over the rectangular

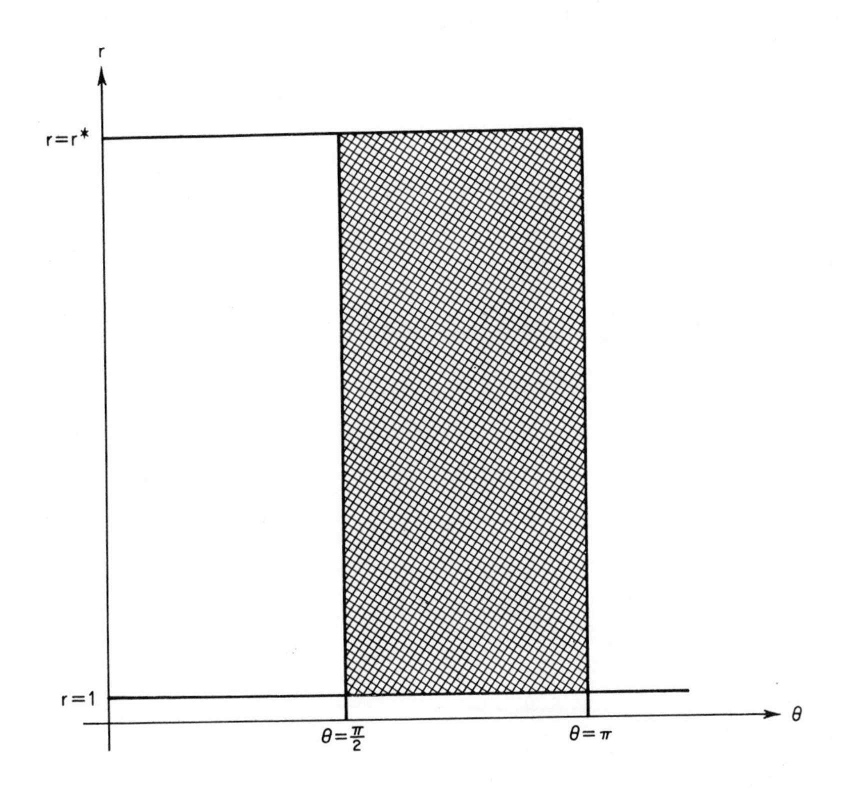

Figure 9.5

region shown in Figure 9. 5. The boundary conditions to be considered are

(9. 21) $$\Omega = 0 \quad \text{for} \quad r = r^*$$

(9. 22) $$\Omega = 0 \quad \text{for} \quad \theta = \frac{\pi}{2}$$

(9. 23) $$\frac{\partial \Omega}{\partial \theta} = 0 \quad \text{for} \quad \theta = \pi$$

(9. 24) $$\frac{\partial \Omega}{\partial r} = - \cos \theta \quad \text{for} \quad r = 1 .$$

This maximization was carried out [180] for $r^* = 30$ in the same spirit as for minimal surfaces in Section 9. 2. For a variety of values of V_∞, streamlines were produced similar to those shown in Figure 9. 6. However,

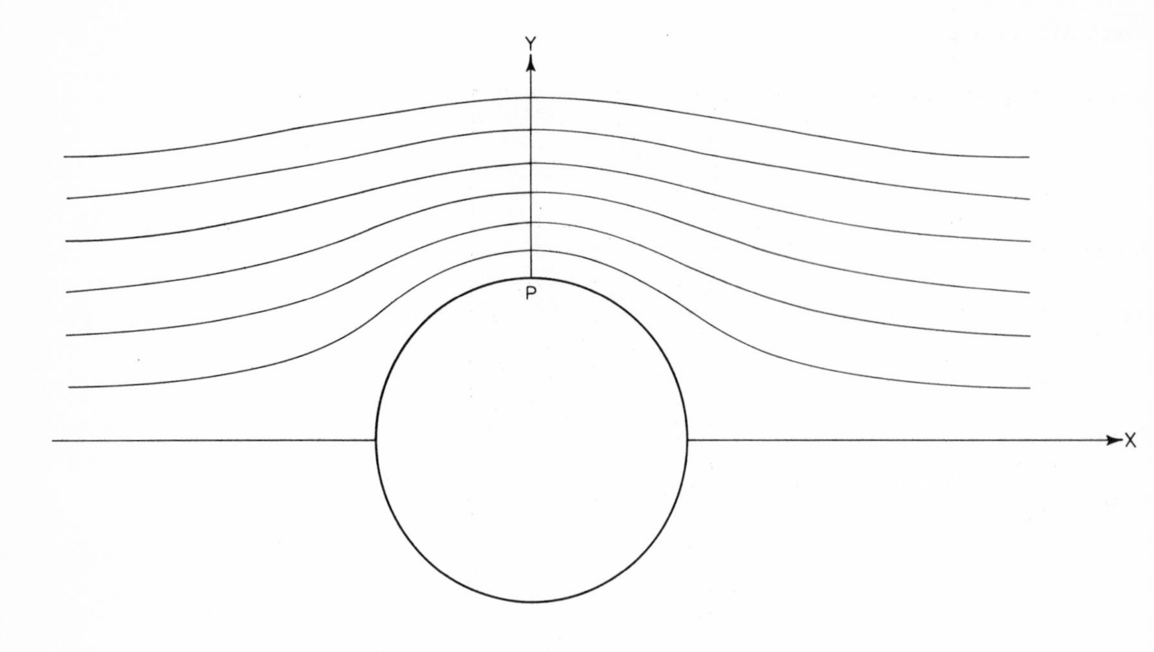

Figure 9.6

for certain values of V_∞, the numerical results were at first inexplicable. In order to discuss these let us first consider a theorem of M. Shiffman [389]. Shiffman proved that for the exterior boundary value problem (9. 10) - (9. 12) there exists a critical Mach number M_∞^* such that for any $M_\infty < M_\infty^*$ there is a uniquely determined completely subsonic flow with free stream Mach number M_∞ and no circulation about S. Moreover, as $M_\infty \to M_\infty^*$ from below, the first place at which the velocity becomes sonic is the point P shown in Figure 9. 6.

Our numerical method was then applied in a sequence of problems which allowed V_∞ to increase. In terms of the Mach number, it was then ound numerically that the velocity first became sonic at P for $M_\infty = 0.404$, which is then an approximation for Shiffman's critical Mach number. nterestingly enough, however, the entire numerical method still continued o give answers for M_∞ in the range

$$0.404 < M_\infty < 0.431.$$

Numerical calculations in this range showed that there was a small bubble area in which the velocity was supersonic, outside of which the velocity was subsonic, and on the boundary of which the velocity was sonic (see Figure 9.7.) And after an extensive literature search, it was found that such a configuration had actually been predicted in 1941 by Imai [209].

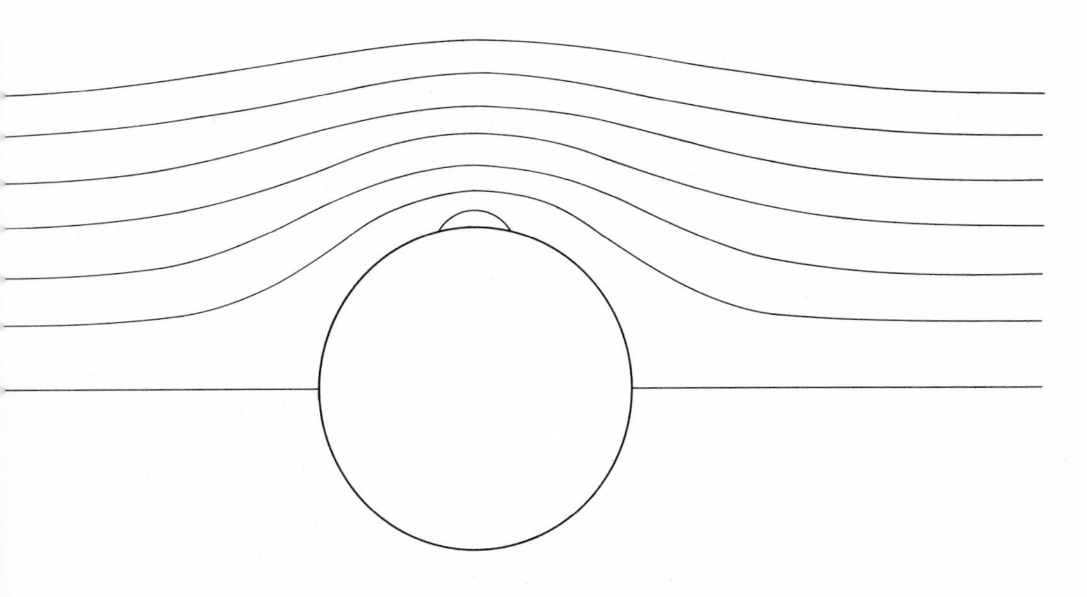

Figure 9.7

Lecture 10 - Steady State Navier Stokes Problems

10.1. Introduction. In the last lecture we discussed a fluid problem which falls properly into the study of gas dynamics. Compressibility played a major role in the model and viscosity was neglected. In this lecture, attention will be directed toward problems in which viscosity plays the major role while compressibility is neglected. Such a situation is considered by many to be basic in the motion of a liquid. And because the problem to be discussed does not have a variational formulation, we shall return to a direct numerical approach.

It should be noted that a trivial, and perhaps annoying, notational problem must be discussed now. In the numerical analysis literature, the symbol ω is used consistently to represent the over-relaxation factor in the generalized Newton's method, while in the fluid dynamics literature it is used consistently to represent vorticity. In these lectures we have elected to let ω represent vorticity.

10.2. Statement of the Analytical Problem. The problem to be considered can be formulated as follows. Other problems can be treated in a similar fashion. Let the points $(0,0)$, $(1,0)$, $(1,1)$ and $(0,1)$ be denoted by A, B, C and D, respectively (see Figure 10.1). Let S be the square whose vertices are A, B, C, D and denote its interior by R. On R the equations of motion to be satisfied are the two dimensional, steady state, Navier-Stokes equations, that is

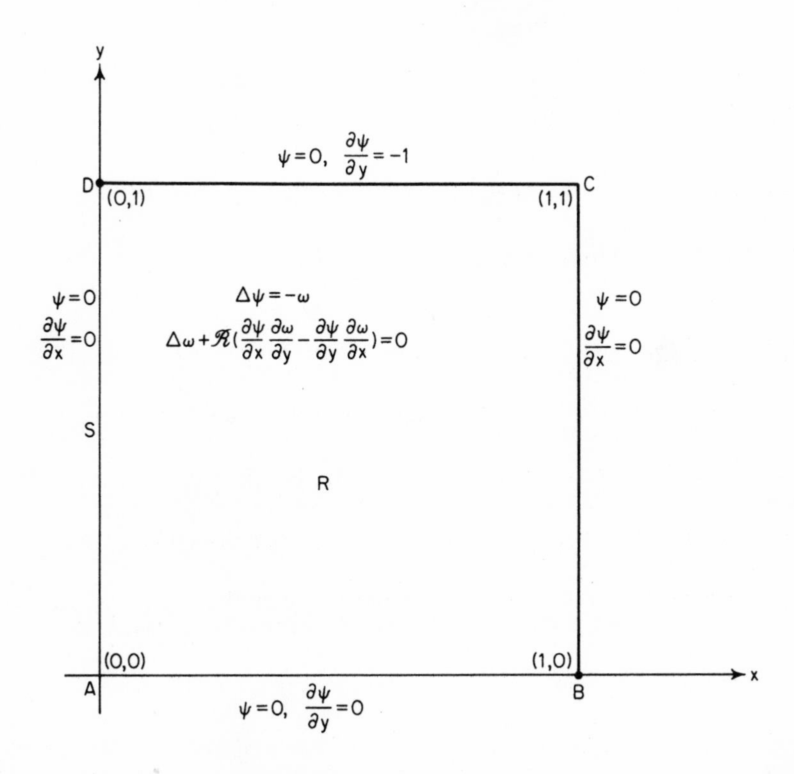

Figure 10.1

(10.1)
$$\Delta\psi = -\omega$$

(10.2)
$$\Delta\omega + \mathcal{R}\left(\frac{\partial\psi}{\partial x}\frac{\partial\omega}{\partial y} - \frac{\partial\psi}{\partial y}\frac{\partial\omega}{\partial x}\right) = 0 ,$$

where ψ is the stream function, ω is the vorticity, and $\mathcal{R}$ is the Reynolds number. On S the boundary conditions to be satisfied are

(10.3)
$$\psi = 0 , \quad \frac{\partial\psi}{\partial x} = 0 , \qquad \text{on AD}$$

(10.4)
$$\psi = 0 , \quad \frac{\partial\psi}{\partial y} = 0 , \qquad \text{on AB}$$

(10. 5) $\qquad \psi = 0, \quad \dfrac{\partial \psi}{\partial x} = 0, \quad$ on BC

(10.6) $\qquad \psi = 0, \quad \dfrac{\partial \psi}{\partial y} = -1, \quad$ on CD

The analytical problem is defined on $R + S$ by (10. 1) - (10. 6) and is shown diagramatically in Figure 10. 1.

10. 3. Difference Approximations. It will be convenient in this section to recall or to develop several useful finite difference approximations.

With regard to the Navier-Stokes equations, let $h > 0$ and consider the five points (x, y), $(x+h, y)$, $(x, y+h)$, $(x-h, y)$, $(x, y-h)$, numbered 0, 1, 2, 3, 4, respectively in Figure 10. 2. Suppose first that $\omega(x, y)$ is defined

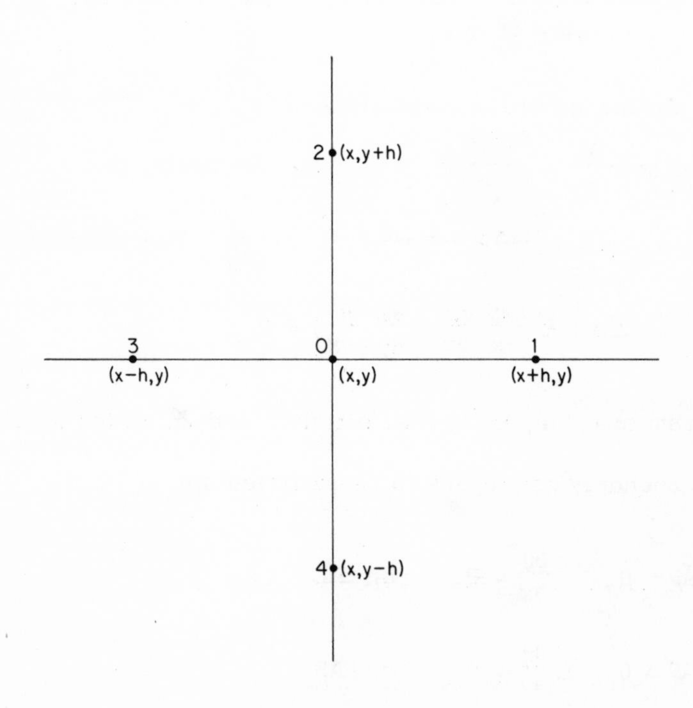

Figure 10. 2

: the point numbered 0 in Figure 10. 2. Then (10. 1) will be approximated

y

0. 7) $$-4\psi_0 + \psi_1 + \psi_2 + \psi_3 + \psi_4 = -h^2\omega_0 .$$

ext, suppose that $\psi(x,y)$ is defined at the points numbered 0, 1, 2, 3, 4 in igure 10. 2. Then (10. 2) can be approximated first by the difference-ifferential equation

0. 8) $$-4\omega_0+\omega_1+\omega_2+\omega_3+\omega_4+h^2\mathcal{R}\left(\frac{\psi_1-\psi_3}{2h}\frac{\partial\omega}{\partial y}-\frac{\psi_2-\psi_4}{2h}\frac{\partial\omega}{\partial x}\right) = 0 .$$

or simplicity, in (10. 8) set

$$\alpha = \psi_1 - \psi_3$$

$$\beta = \psi_2 - \psi_4 .$$

hen, to assure the dominance of the coefficient of ω_0, set $\frac{\partial\omega}{\partial y} = \frac{\omega_2-\omega_0}{h}$ n (10. 8) if $\alpha \geq 0$, or set $\frac{\partial\omega}{\partial y} = \frac{\omega_0-\omega_4}{h}$ if $\alpha < 0$. Similarly, set $\frac{\omega}{x} = \frac{\omega_0-\omega_3}{h}$ if $\beta \geq 0$, or set $\frac{\partial\omega}{\partial x} = \frac{\omega_1-\omega_0}{h}$ if $\beta < 0$. Thus, depending n the signs of α and β, (10. 2) will be approximated by the following:

10. 9) $$\left(-4-\frac{\alpha\mathcal{R}}{2}-\frac{\beta\mathcal{R}}{2}\right)\omega_0+\omega_1+\left(1+\frac{\alpha\mathcal{R}}{2}\right)\omega_2+\left(1+\frac{\beta\mathcal{R}}{2}\right)\omega_3+\omega_4 = 0; \quad \alpha \geq 0,\ \beta \geq 0$$

10. 10) $$\left(-4-\frac{\alpha\mathcal{R}}{2}+\frac{\beta\mathcal{R}}{2}\right)\omega_0+\left(1-\frac{\beta\mathcal{R}}{2}\right)\omega_1+\left(1+\frac{\alpha\mathcal{R}}{2}\right)\omega_2+\omega_3+\omega_4 = 0; \quad \alpha \geq 0,\ \beta < 0$$

10. 11) $$\left(-4+\frac{\alpha\mathcal{R}}{2}-\frac{\beta\mathcal{R}}{2}\right)\omega_0+\omega_1+\omega_2+\left(1+\frac{\beta\mathcal{R}}{2}\right)\omega_3+\left(1-\frac{\alpha\mathcal{R}}{2}\right)\omega_4 = 0; \quad \alpha < 0,\ \beta \geq 0$$

10. 12) $$\left(-4+\frac{\alpha\mathcal{R}}{2}+\frac{\beta\mathcal{R}}{2}\right)\omega_0+\left(1-\frac{\beta\mathcal{R}}{2}\right)\omega_1+\omega_2+\omega_3+\left(1-\frac{\alpha\mathcal{R}}{2}\right)\omega_4 = 0; \quad \alpha < 0,\ \beta < 0 .$$

Next, recall that for three points (x, y), $(x+h, y)$, $(x+2h, y)$, numbered $0, 1, 2$, respectively, in Figure 10. 3(a), one has the approximation [289]

$$\left.\frac{\partial\psi}{\partial x}\right|_0 = \frac{1}{2h}(-3\psi_0 + 4\psi_1 - \psi_2); \tag{10.13a}$$

for three points (x, y), $(x, y+h)$, $(x, y+2h)$, numbered $0, 1, 2$, respectively, in Figure 10. 3(b), one has the approximation

$$\left.\frac{\partial\psi}{\partial y}\right|_0 = \frac{1}{2h}(-3\psi_0 + 4\psi_1 - \psi_2); \tag{10.13b}$$

for three points (x, y), $(x-h, y)$, $(x-2h, y)$, numbered $0, 1, 2$, respectively, in Figure 10. 3(c), one has the approximation

$$\left.\frac{\partial\psi}{\partial x}\right|_0 = \frac{1}{2h}(3\psi_0 - 4\psi_1 + \psi_2); \tag{10.13c}$$

and that for three points (x, y), $(x, y-h)$, $(x, y-2h)$, numbered $0, 1, 2$, respectively, in Figure 10. 3(d), one has

$$\left.\frac{\partial\psi}{\partial x}\right|_0 = \frac{1}{2h}(3\psi_0 - 4\psi_1 + \psi_2). \tag{10.13d}$$

Finally, let us develop approximations for the Laplace operator $\psi_{xx} + \psi_{yy}$ on S in terms of certain function values and normal derivatives.

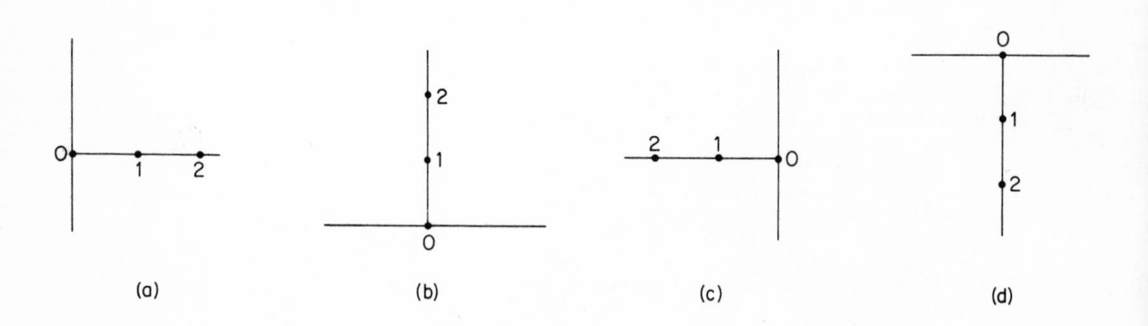

Figure 10.3

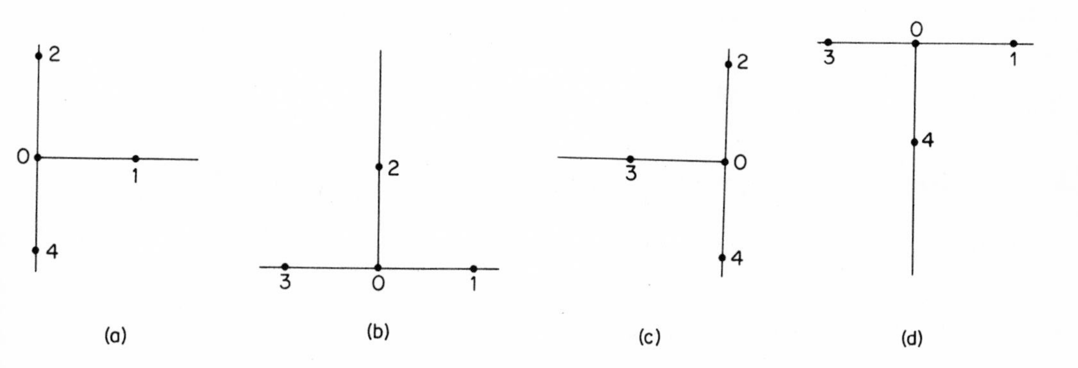

Figure 10.4

Consider the four points (x, y), (x+h, y), (x, y+h), (x, y−h), numbered 0, 1, 2, 4, respectively, in Figure 10.4(a), and let us try to determine parameters $\alpha_0, \alpha_1, \alpha_2, \alpha_4, \alpha_5$ such that

$$(10.14)\qquad (\psi_{xx} + \psi_{yy})|_0 = \alpha_0\psi_0 + \alpha_1\psi_1 + \alpha_2\psi_2 + \alpha_4\psi_4 + \alpha_5\left(\frac{\partial\psi}{\partial x}\right)\Big|_0 .$$

In (10.14), expansion of ψ_1, ψ_2 and ψ_4 into Taylor series about the point numbered 0 and reorganization of terms implies

$$\begin{aligned}(\psi_{xx} + \psi_{yy})|_0 &= \psi_0(\alpha_0 + \alpha_1 + \alpha_2 + \alpha_4)\\ &+ \psi_x(h\alpha_1 + \alpha_5)\\ &+ \psi_y(h\alpha_2 - h\alpha_4)\\ &+ \psi_{xx}\left(\frac{h^2}{2}\alpha_1\right)\\ &+ \psi_{yy}\left(\frac{h^2}{2}\alpha_2 + \frac{h^2}{2}\alpha_4\right)\\ &+ \cdots\cdots \quad .\end{aligned}$$

In this latter equality, the setting of corresponding terms equal yields

$$\alpha_0 + \alpha_1 + \alpha_2 + \alpha_4 = 0$$

$$h\alpha_1 + \alpha_5 = 0$$

$$h\alpha_2 - h\alpha_4 = 0$$

$$\frac{h^2}{2}\alpha_1 = 1$$

$$\frac{h^2}{2}\alpha_2 + \frac{h^2}{2}\alpha_4 = 1 ,$$

the solution of which is

$$\alpha_0 = -\frac{4}{h^2}, \quad \alpha_1 = \frac{2}{h^2}, \quad \alpha_2 = \alpha_4 = \frac{1}{h^2}, \quad \alpha_5 = -\frac{2}{h} .$$

Thus one arrives at the following approximation:

$$(10.15a) \qquad (\psi_{xx} + \psi_{yy})|_0 = -\frac{4}{h^2}\psi_0 + \frac{2}{h^2}\psi_1 + \frac{1}{h^2}\psi_2 + \frac{1}{h^2}\psi_4 - \frac{2}{h}\left(\frac{\partial\psi}{\partial x}\right)|_0 .$$

Similarly, for the four points (x, y), $(x+h, y)$, $(x, y+h)$, $(x-h, y)$, numbered 0, 1, 2, 3, respectively, in Figure 10. 4(b), one has

$$(10.15b) \qquad (\psi_{xx} + \psi_{yy})|_0 = -\frac{4}{h^2}\psi_0 + \frac{1}{h^2}\psi_1 + \frac{2}{h^2}\psi_2 + \frac{1}{h^2}\psi_3 - \frac{2}{h}\left(\frac{\partial\psi}{\partial y}\right)|_0 ;$$

for the four points (x, y), $(x, y+h)$, $(x-h, y)$, $(x, y-h)$, numbered 0, 2, 3, 4, respectively, in Figure 10. 4(c), one has

$$(10.15c) \qquad (\psi_{xx} + \psi_{yy})|_0 = -\frac{4}{h^2}\psi_0 + \frac{1}{h^2}\psi_2 + \frac{2}{h^2}\psi_3 + \frac{1}{h^2}\psi_4 + \frac{2}{h}\left(\frac{\partial\psi}{\partial x}\right)|_0 ;$$

and for the four points (x, y), $(x+h, y)$, $(x-h, y)$, $(x, y-h)$, numbered 0, 1, 3, 4, respectively, in Figure 3. 4(d), one has

$$(10.15d) \qquad (\psi_{xx} + \psi_{yy})|_0 = -\frac{4}{h^2}\psi_0 + \frac{1}{h^2}\psi_1 + \frac{1}{h^2}\psi_3 + \frac{2}{h^2}\psi_4 + \frac{2}{h}\left(\frac{\partial\psi}{\partial y}\right)|_0 .$$

Note that the numbering of the points in Figure 10.4 is consistent with that in Figure 10.2.

10.4. The Numerical Method. For a fixed positive integer n, set $h = \frac{1}{n}$ starting at $(0, 0)$ with grid size h, construct and number in the usual way the set of interior grid points R_h and the set of boundary grid points S_h. To within some preassigned tolerance ϵ, we aim to find a solution $\psi^{(k)}$ of (10.7) on R_h and a solution $\omega^{(k)}$ of (10.9) - (10.12) on $R_h + S_h$, subject to the boundary restrictions on ψ, and we proceed as follows.

Denote by $R_{h,1}$ those points of R_h whose distance from S is h, and denote by $R_{h,2}$ those points of R_h whose distance from S is greater than h. Initially, set

$$\psi^{(0)} = C_1, \quad \text{on } R_h \tag{10.16}$$

$$\omega^{(0)} = C_2, \quad \text{on } R_h + S_h, \tag{10.17}$$

where C_1 and C_2 are constants. A modified over-relaxation procedure which does not require much storage to obtain the desired result is then applied as follows to yield $\psi^{(1)}$ from $\psi^{(0)}$ and $\omega^{(0)}$. On R_h, set

$$\psi^{(1,0)} = \psi^{(0)} \tag{10.18}$$

and on $R_{h,2}$ generate $\bar{\psi}^{(1,1)}$ by sweeping along each row of $R_{h,2}$ from left to right, starting from the bottom row and proceeding to the top row, by the recursion formula

$$\bar{\psi}_0^{(1,j)} = (1-r_\psi)\psi_0^{(1,j-1)} + \frac{r_\psi}{4}[\psi_1^{(1,j-1)} + \psi_2^{(1,j-1)} + \bar{\psi}_3^{(1,j)} + \bar{\psi}_4^{(1,j)} + h^2\omega_0], \tag{10.19}$$

where $0 < r_\psi < 2$. After each such sweep, $\psi^{(1,j)}$ is defined on $R_{h,2}$ by the weighted average

(10.20) $$\psi^{(1,j)} = \xi \psi^{(1,j-1)} + (1-\xi)\bar{\psi}^{(1,j)}, \qquad 0 \le \xi \le 1$$

This inner iteration process continues until, for the given tolerance ϵ, one has

(10.21) $$|\psi^{(1,k)} - \psi^{(1,k+1)}| < \epsilon ,$$

from which one defines on $R_{h,2}$

(10.22) $$\psi^{(1)} = \psi^{(1,k)}$$

In order to define $\psi^{(1)}$ on $R_{h,1}$, we apply (10.13a-10.13d) and (10.3) - (10.6) in the following fashion. At each point of $R_{h,1}$ of the form (ih, h), $i = 1, 2, \ldots, n-1$, set (in the notation of Figure 10.3(b))

(10.23a) $$\psi_1^{(1)} = \frac{\psi_2^{(1)}}{4}$$

Similarly, at each point of $R_{h,1}$ of the form (h, ih), $i = 2, 3, \ldots, n-2$, set (in the notation of Figure 10.3(a))

(10.23b) $$\psi_1^{(1)} = \frac{\psi_2^{(1)}}{4} ,$$

while at each point of $R_{h,1}$ of the form $(1-h, ih)$, $i = 2, 3, \ldots, n-2$, set (in the notation of Figure 10.3(c))

(10.23c) $$\psi_1^{(1)} = \frac{\psi_2^{(1)}}{4}$$

Finally, at each point of $R_{h,1}$ of the form $(ih, 1-h)$, $i = 1, 2, \ldots, n-1$, set (in the notation of Figure 10. 3(d))

(10. 23d) $$\psi_1^{(1)} = \frac{h}{2} + \frac{\psi_2^{(1)}}{4} .$$

Thus, (10. 22) and (10. 23a) - (10. 23d) define $\psi^{(1)}$ on all of R_h.

Next, proceed to construct $\omega^{(1)}$ on $R_h + S_h$ as follows. On S_h, use (10. 1), (10. 3) - (10. 6) and (10. 15a) - (10. 15d) to yield at each point (ih, 0), $i = 0, 1, 2, \ldots, n$ (in the notation of Figure 10. 4(b))

(10. 24a) $$\bar{\omega}_0^{(1)} = -\frac{2\psi_2^{(1)}}{h^2}$$

at each point (0, ih), $i = 1, 2, \ldots, n-1$, in the notation of Figure 10. 4(a)

(10. 24b) $$\bar{\omega}_0^{(1)} = -\frac{2\psi_1^{(1)}}{h^2} ;$$

at each point (1, ih), $i = 1, 2, \ldots, n-1$, in the notation of Figure 10. 4(c)

(10. 24c) $$\bar{\omega}_0^{(1)} = -\frac{2\psi_3^{(1)}}{h^2}$$

and, at each point (ih, 1), $i = 0, 1, 2, \ldots, n$, in the notation of Figure 10. 4(d)

(10. 24d) $$\bar{\omega}_0^{(1)} = \frac{2}{h} - \frac{2\psi_4^{(1)}}{h^2} .$$

One then defines $\omega^{(1)}$ on S_h by the weighted average formula

(10. 25) $$\omega^{(1)} = \delta\omega^{(0)} + (1 - \delta)\bar{\omega}^{(1)}, \qquad 0 \le \delta \le 1 .$$

We proceed next to determine $\omega^{(1)}$ on R_h by again using a modified over-relaxation procedure. At each point of S_h set

$$\omega^{(1,0)} = \omega^{(1)}$$

while at each point of R_h set

$$\omega^{(1,0)} = \omega^{(0)}$$

Then generate $\bar{\omega}^{(1,1)}$ by sweeping along each row of R_h from left to right, starting from the bottom row and proceeding to the top row, by the recursion formula

$$(10.26) \quad \bar{\omega}_0^{(1,j)} = (1 - r_\omega)\omega_0^{(1,j-1)} + \frac{r_\omega}{\Omega_0}[\Omega_1 \cdot \omega_1^{(1,j-1)} + \Omega_2 \cdot \omega_2^{(1,j-1)} + \Omega_3 \cdot \bar{\omega}_3^{(1,j)} + \Omega_4 \bar{\omega}_4^{(1,j)}] ,$$

where $0 < r_\omega < 2$, where

$$\Omega_0 = 4 + \frac{\mathcal{R}}{2}|\alpha| + \frac{\mathcal{R}}{2}|\beta|$$

$$\Omega_1 = \begin{cases} 1 , & \beta \geq 0 \\ 1 + \frac{\mathcal{R}}{2}|\beta| , & \beta < 0 , \end{cases}$$

$$\Omega_2 = \begin{cases} 1 + \frac{\mathcal{R}}{2}\alpha , & \alpha \geq 0 \\ 1 , & \alpha < 0 \end{cases}$$

$$\Omega_3 = \begin{cases} 1 + \frac{\mathcal{R}}{2}\beta , & \beta \geq 0 \\ 1 , & \beta < 0 \end{cases}$$

$$\Omega_4 = \begin{cases} 1 , & \alpha \geq 0 \\ 1 + \frac{\mathcal{R}}{2}|\alpha| , & \alpha < 0 \end{cases}$$

and where, as defined previously,

$$\alpha = \psi_1 - \psi_3$$

$$\beta = \psi_2 - \psi_4 .$$

fter each such sweep, $\omega^{(1,j)}$ is defined on R_h by the weighted average

$$\omega^{(1,j)} = \delta\omega^{(1,j-1)} + (1-\delta)\bar{\omega}^{(1,j)}, \qquad 0 \le \delta \le 1 \tag{10.27}$$

here δ is the same weight as that used in (10. 25). This inner iteration ontinues until, for the given tolerance ϵ, one has

$$|\omega^{(1,K)} - \omega^{(1,K+1)}| < \epsilon , \tag{10.28}$$

rom which one defines on R_h

$$\omega^{(1)} = \omega^{(1,K)} . \tag{10.29}$$

Proceed next to determine $\psi^{(2)}$ on R_h from $\omega^{(1)}$ and $\psi^{(1)}$ in the ame fashion as $\psi^{(1)}$ was determined from $\omega^{(0)}$ and $\psi^{(0)}$. Then construct $\omega^{(2)}$ on $R_h + S_h$ from $\omega^{(1)}$ and $\psi^{(2)}$ in the same fashion as $\omega^{(1)}$ was etermined from $\omega^{(0)}$ and $\psi^{(1)}$. In the indicated fashion, construct the inite sequences of outer iterates

$$\psi^{(0)}, \psi^{(1)}, \psi^{(2)}, \ldots, \psi^{(m)}$$

$$\omega^{(0)}, \omega^{(1)}, \omega^{(2)}, \ldots, \omega^{(m)}$$

which satisfy

$$|\psi^{(m)} - \psi^{(m+1)}| < \epsilon, \text{ on } R_h$$

$$|\omega^{(m)} - \omega^{(m+1)}| < \epsilon, \text{ on } R_h + S_h .$$

The discrete functions $\psi^{(m)}$ and $\omega^{(m)}$ are taken to be the numerical approximations of $\psi(x, y)$ and $\omega(x, y)$, respectively, after verifying that they satisfy (10. 7) and (10. 9) - (10. 12).

10. 5. Examples. In Figures 10. 5 - 10. 16 are shown graphically the streamlines and equivorticity curves for $\mathcal{R} = 10, 100, 500, 1000, 3000, 100000$ for the set of parameter values $h = \frac{1}{20}$, $C_1 = C_2 = 0$, $r_\psi = 1.8$, $r_\omega = 1$, $\xi = 0.1$, $\delta = 0.7$. A tolerance of 10^{-4} was taken for convergence of both inner and outer iterations. The outer iterations for each of $\mathcal{R} = 10, 500, 1000, 3000, 100000$ converged in fewer than ten minutes and the number of outer iterations required were, respectively, 10, 25, 20, 16, 14. The case $\mathcal{R} = 100$ was allowed only twelve minutes of running time at the end of which 40 iterations had elapsed and convergence to $6 \cdot 10^{-4}$ had resulted.

It was clear that for convergence ξ and δ depended on h. For fixed $C_1 = C_2 = 0$ and $r_\psi = 1.8$, $r_\omega = 1$, the following results were found. Outer iteration convergence was achieved for $h = \frac{1}{8}$, $\xi = \delta = 0$, but outer iteration divergence resulted in every case for $h \le \frac{1}{10}$, $\xi = \delta = 0$. For $h = \frac{1}{16}$, outer iteration convergence was achieved with the choice $\xi = \delta = 0.1$, but outer iteration convergence was greatly accelerated as δ was allowed to increase. For $h = \frac{1}{20}$, all choices of $\xi \le 0.1$, $\delta \le 0.5$ resulted in outer iteration divergence. Further experimentation into the relationships between ξ, δ, h, convergence, and divergence was deemed to be of great interest but too costly to be run at the present time.

Occasionally, the method did not converge because an inner iteration did not converge. When this happened, invariably the choice of r_ω was at fault and a new choice was made after several trial values were tested. The choices $r_\psi = 1.8$ and $r_\omega = 1$ were finally decided upon because they worked well uniformly, even though inner iteration convergence could often be accelerated by different choices.

In cases where the outer iterations were diverging, no choices of C_1 and C_2 ever resulted in convergence.

With regard to the physics of the problem, it should be observed that Figures 10.11 - 10.16 indicate clearly that the vorticity is becoming uniform in a large connected subregion of the given region, as was predicted theoretically by Batchelor [22].

It is also important to note that the method of Section 10.4 is only one of several closely related convergent methods (see, e.g., [179]). These can be obtained by eliminating the application of special formulas (10.23a)-(10.23d) on the first inner ring of grid points and/or by averaging after achieving the convergence of each inner iteration rather than after each pass, as is accomplished by (10.19), (10.20), (10.26) and (10.27). The relative merits of these various methods are still to be explored.

Finally, note that it would be of interest to apply the steady state method of this lecture in the spirit of Lectures 6 and 7 to non-steady state problems.

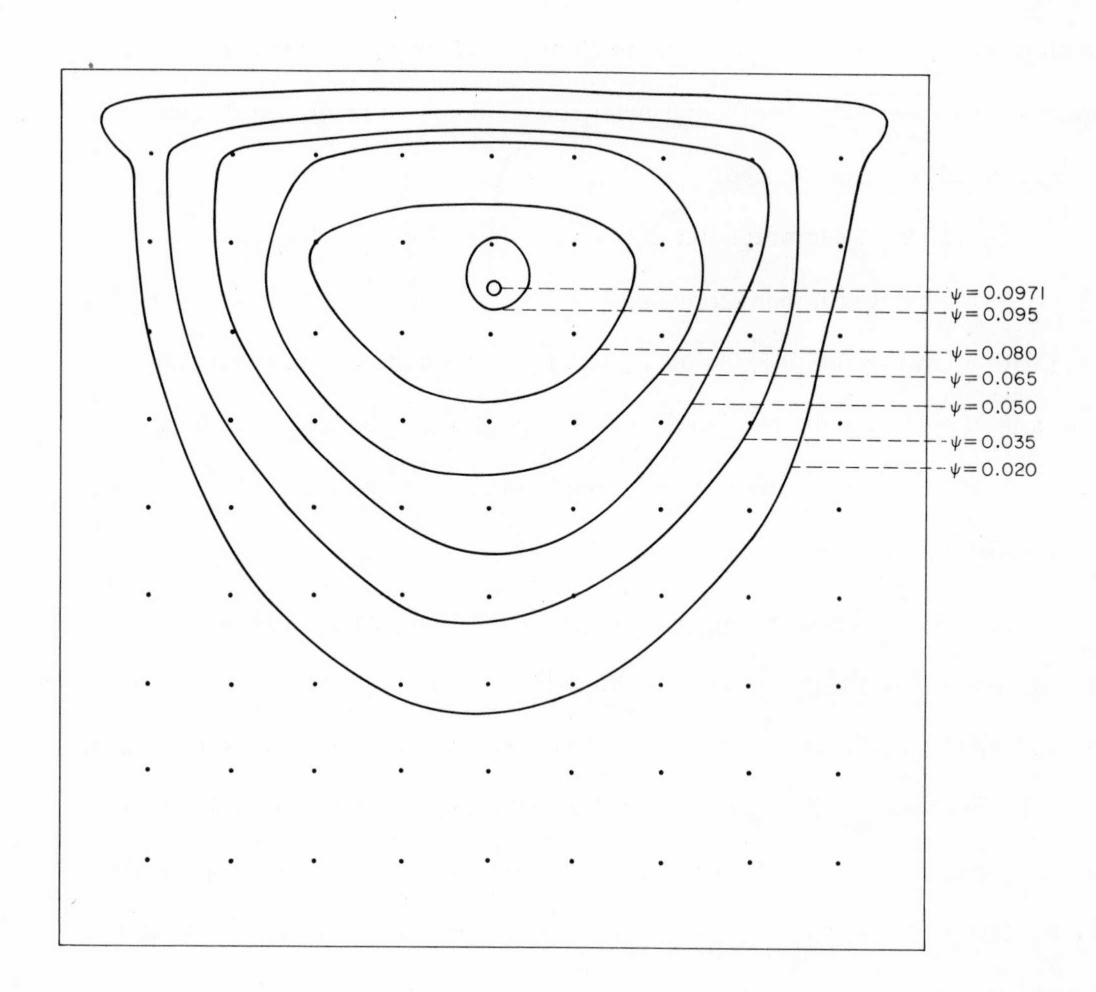

Figure 10.5. STREAMLINES FOR REYNOLDS NUMBER 10

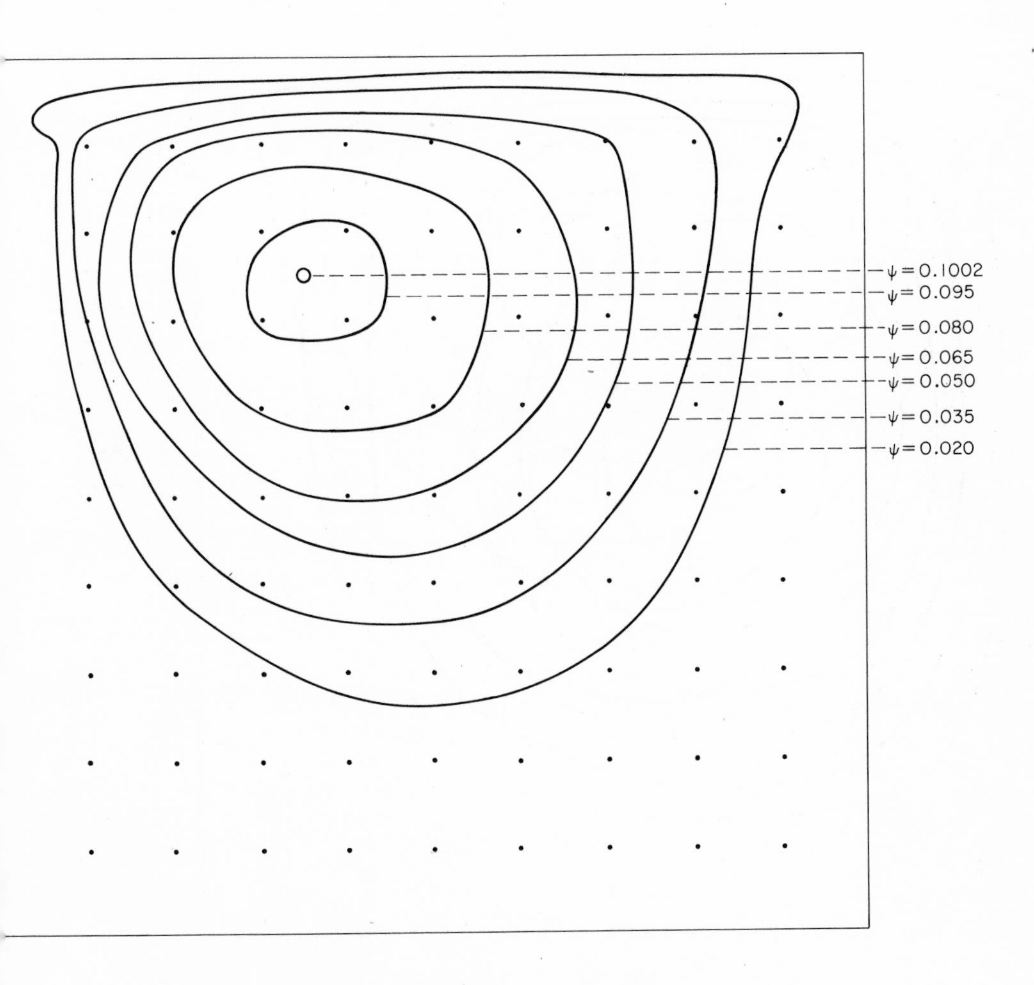

Figure 10.6. STREAMLINES FOR REYNOLDS NUMBER 100

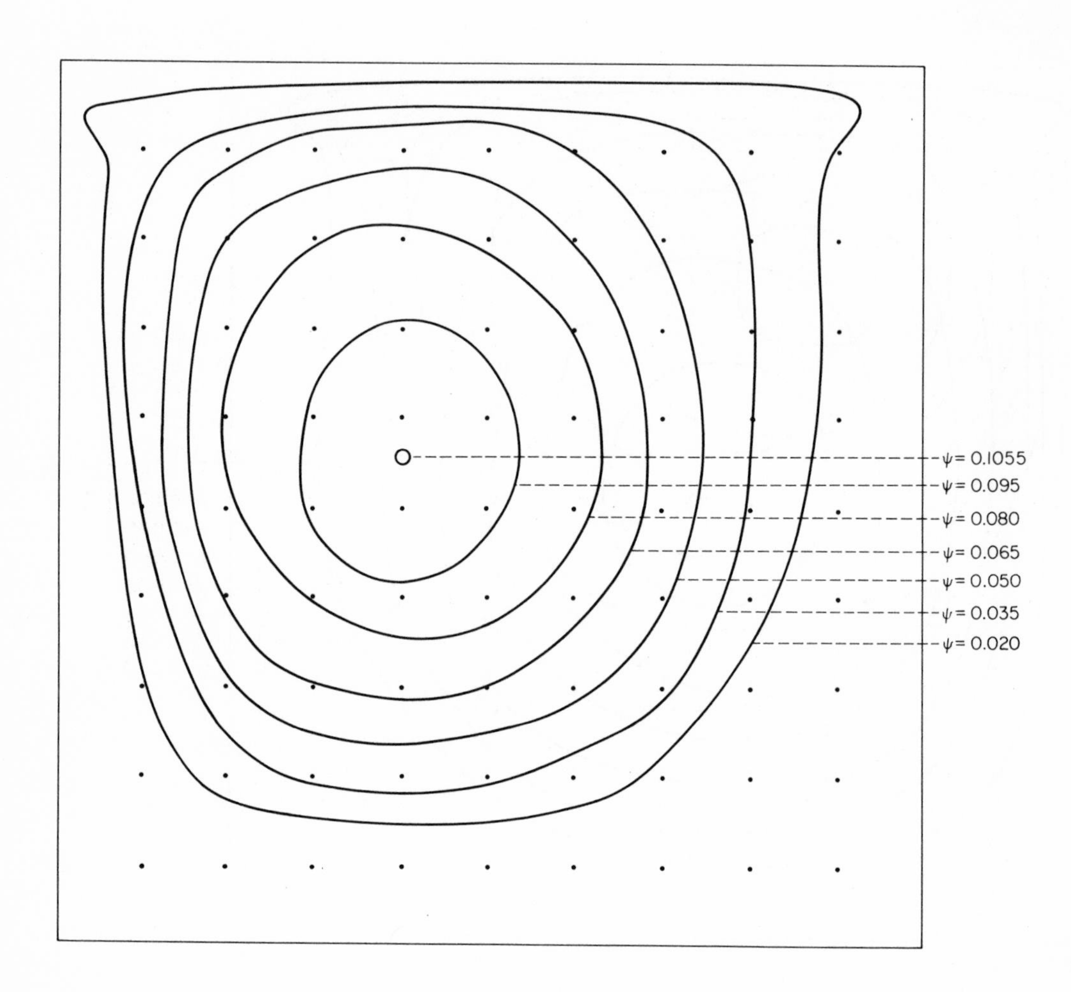

Figure 10.7. STREAMLINES FOR REYNOLDS NUMBER 500

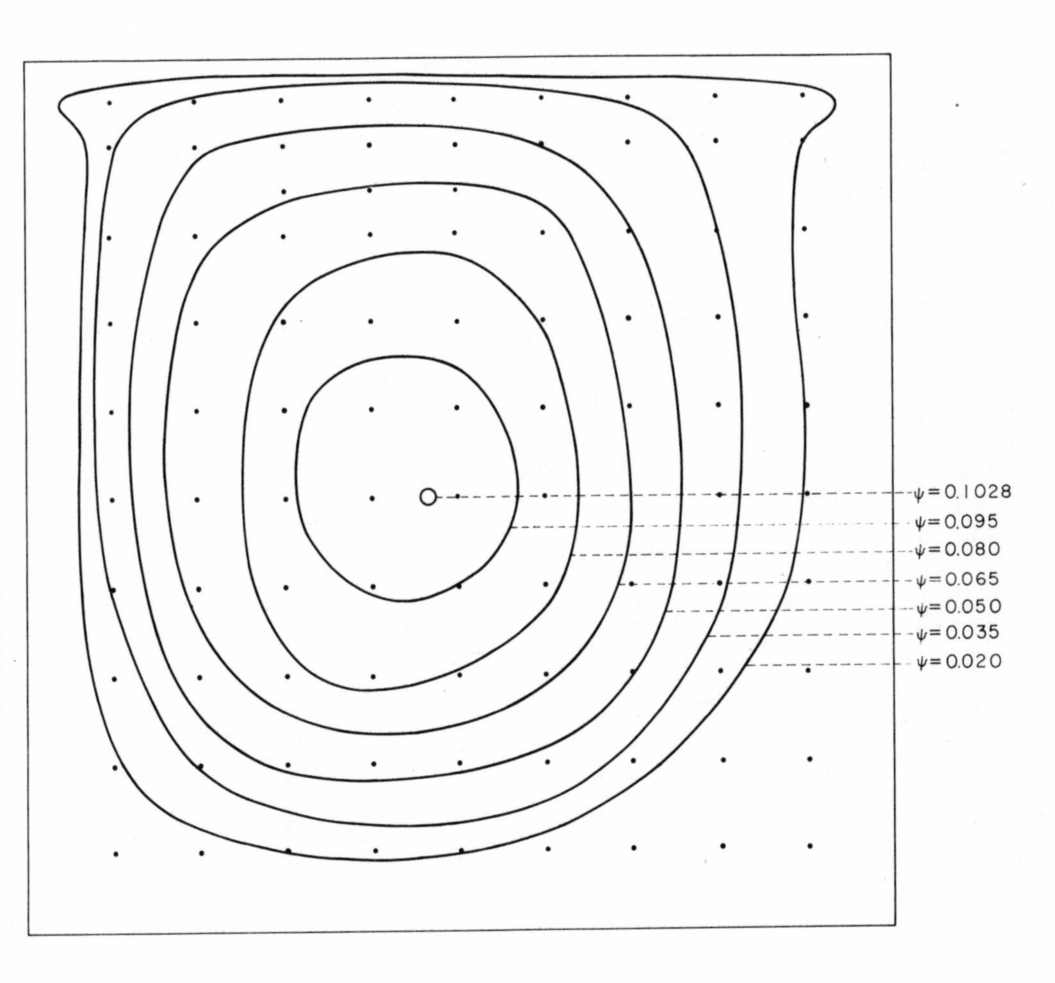

Figure 10.8. STREAMLINES FOR REYNOLDS NUMBER 1000

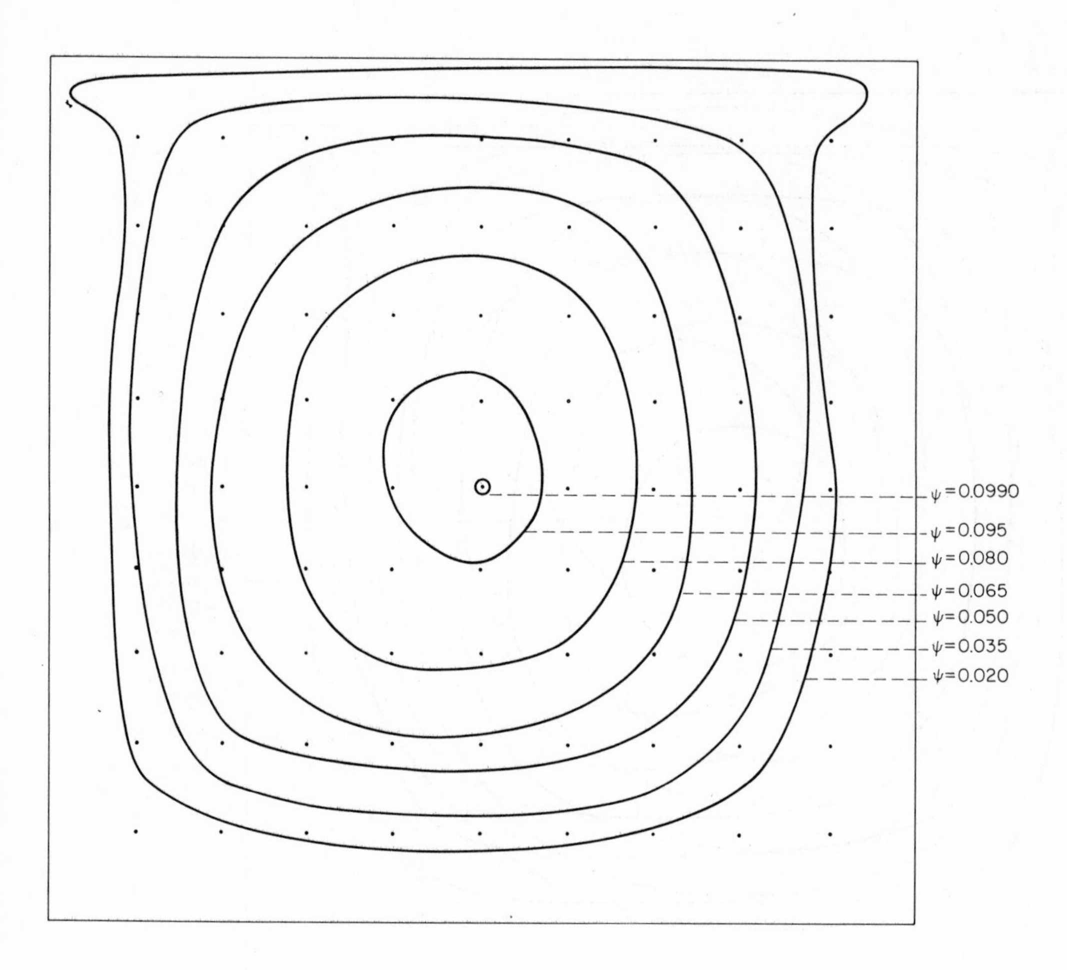

Figure 10.9. STREAMLINES FOR REYNOLDS NUMBER 3000

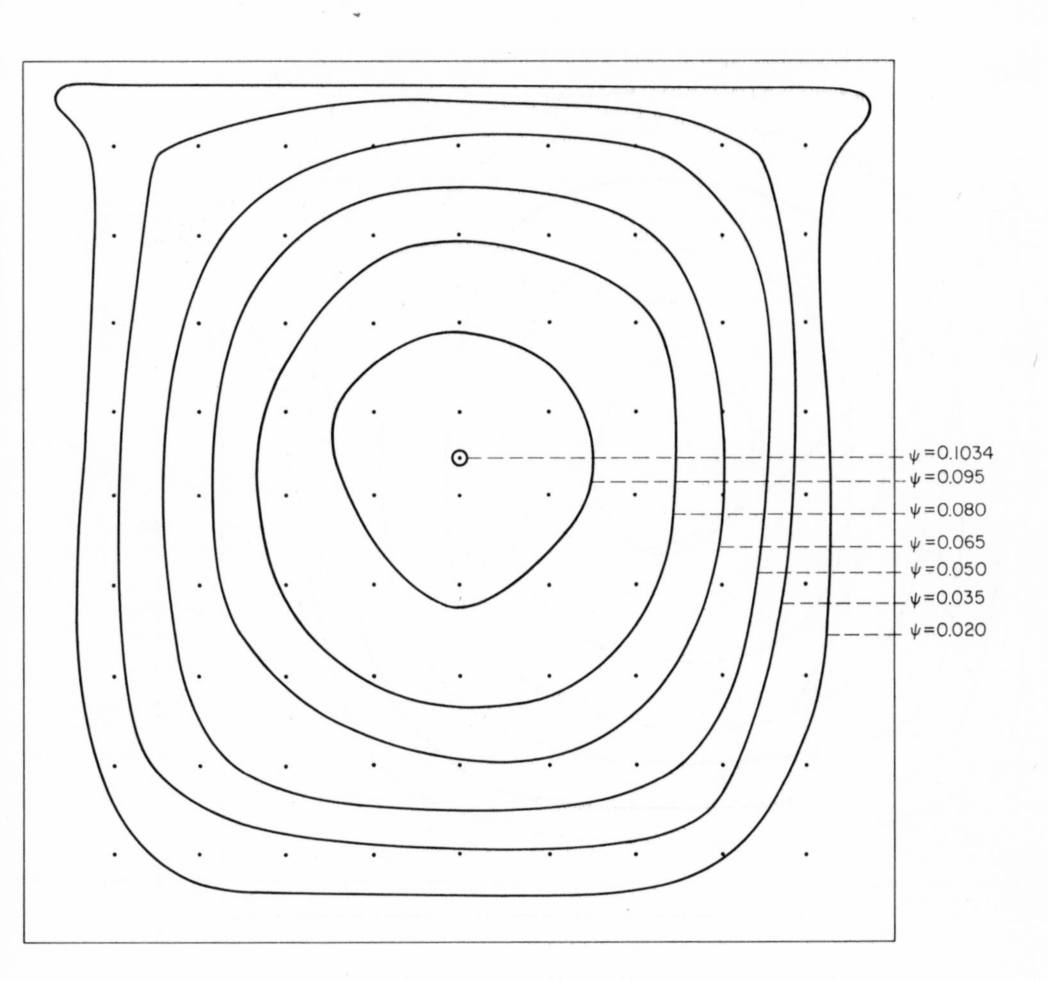

FIGURE 10.10. STREAMLINES FOR REYNOLDS NUMBER 100,000

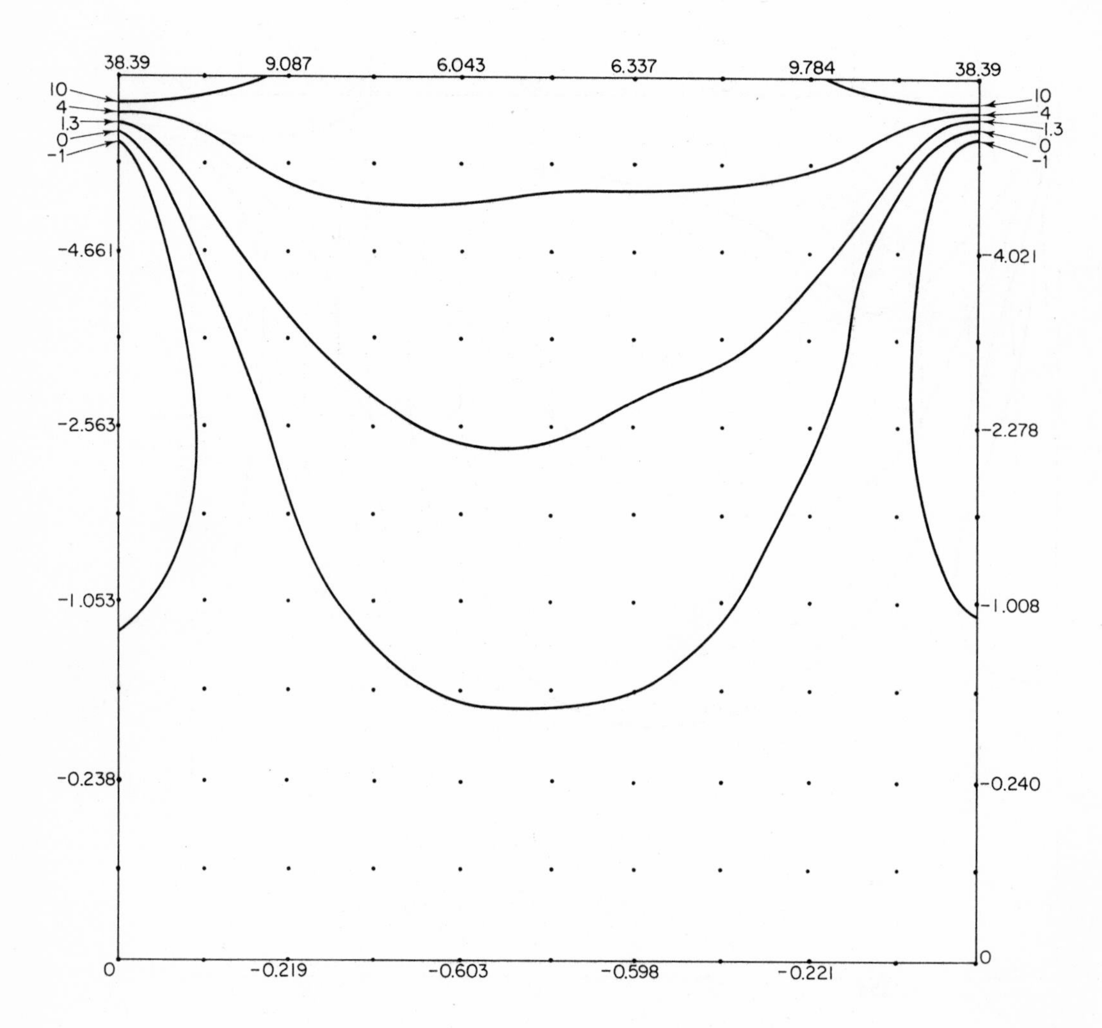

FIGURE 10.11. EQUIVORTICITY CURVES FOR REYNOLDS NUMBER 10

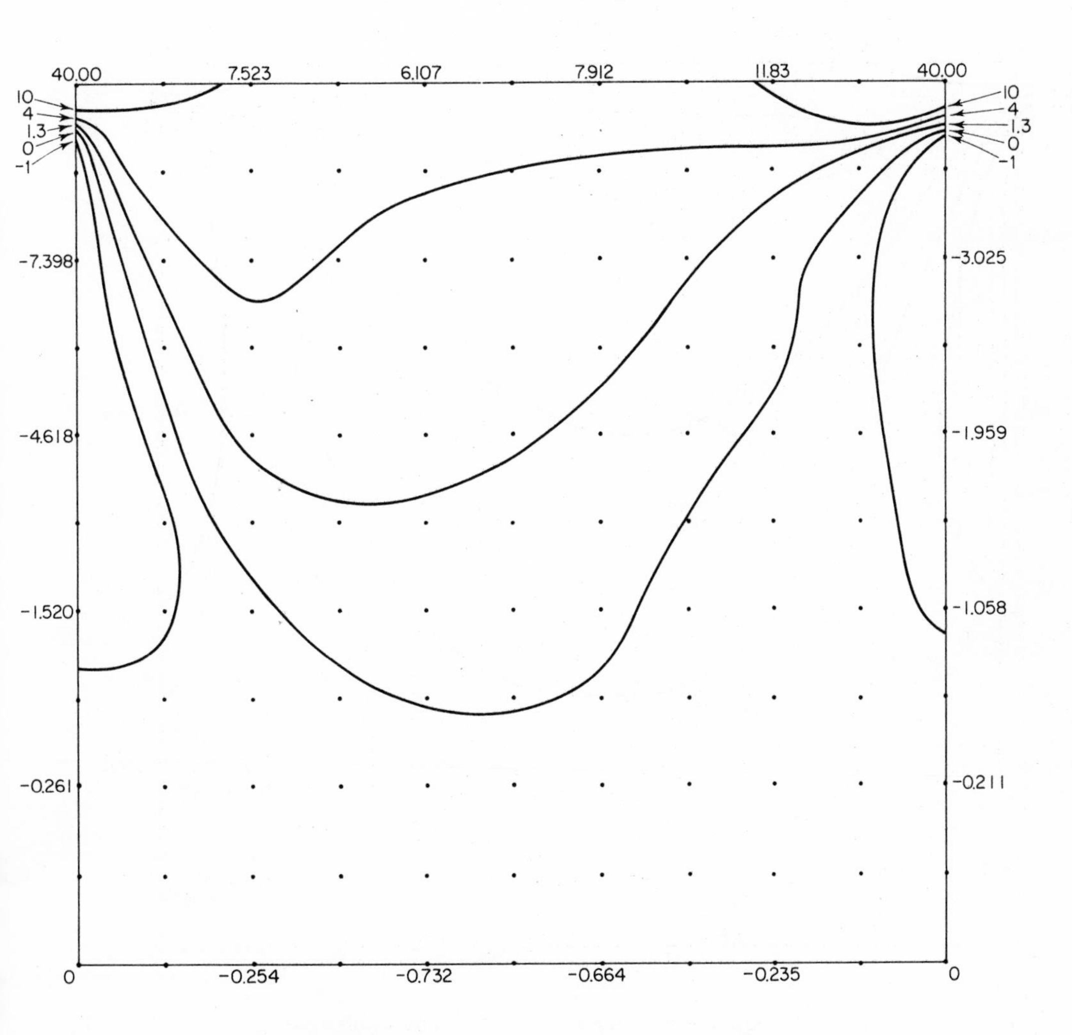

FIGURE 10.12. EQUIVORTICITY CURVES FOR REYNOLDS NUMBER 100

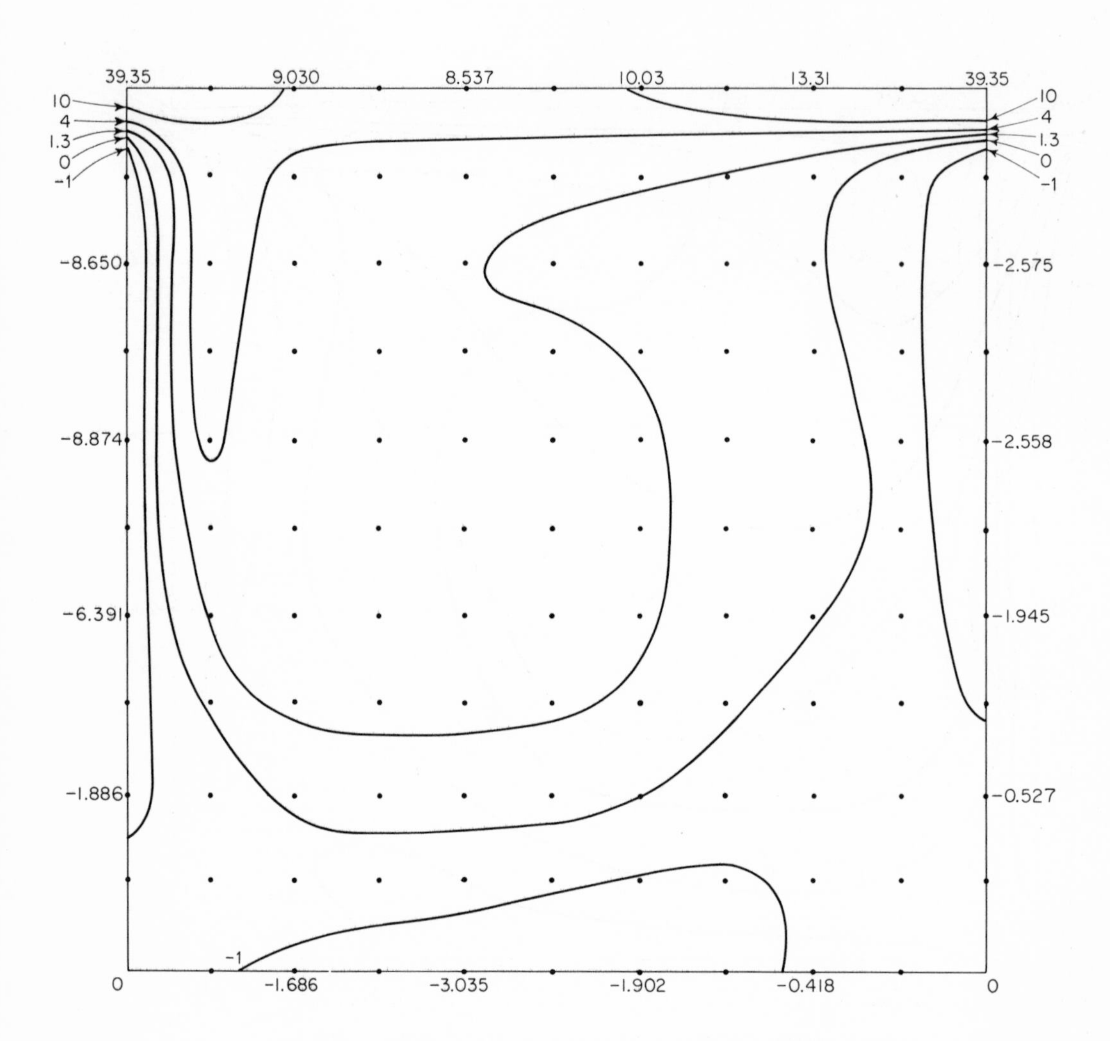

FIGURE 10.13. EQUIVORTICITY CURVES FOR REYNOLDS NUMBER 500

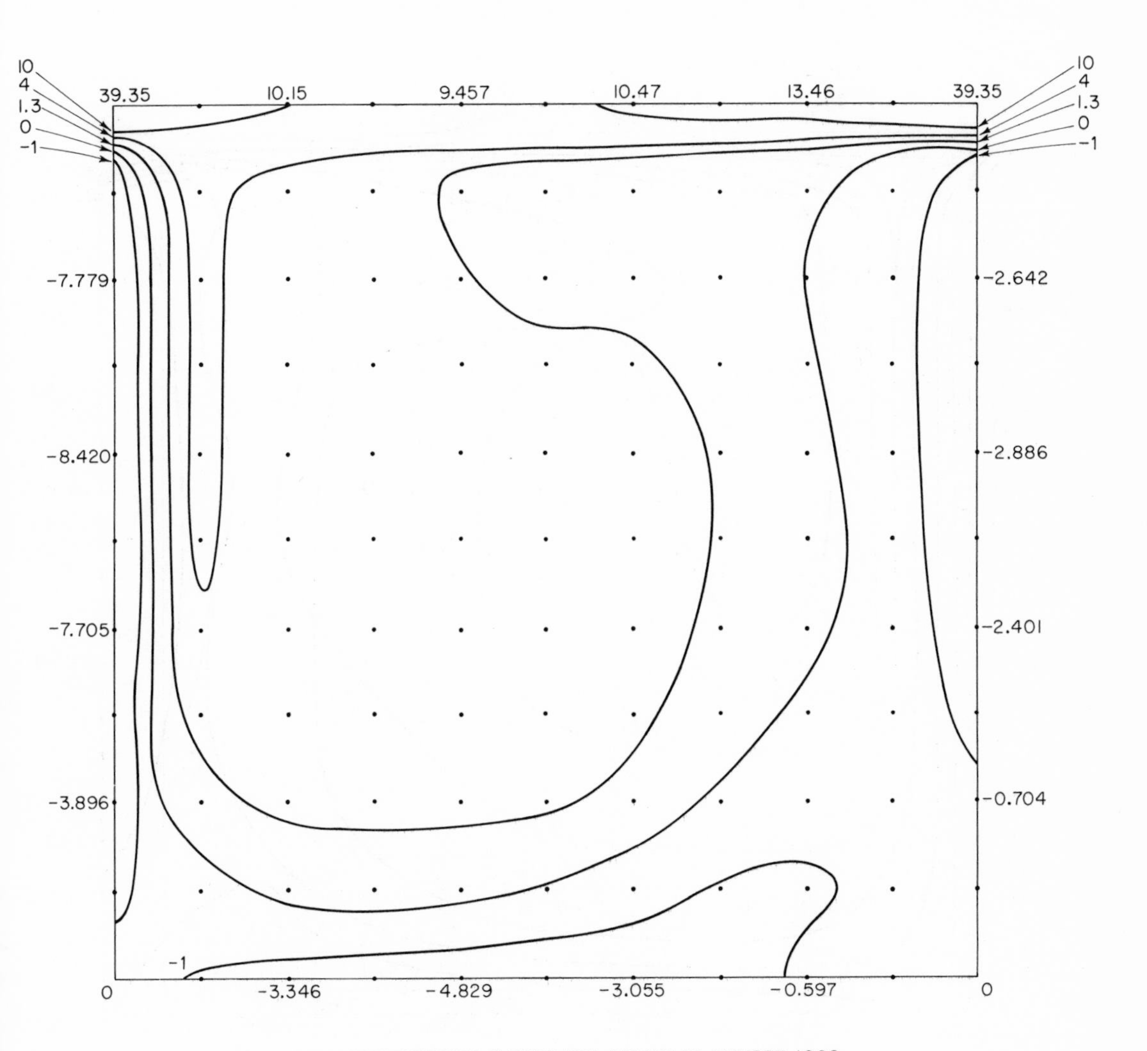

Figure 10.14. EQUIVORTICITY CURVES FOR REYNOLDS NUMBER 1000

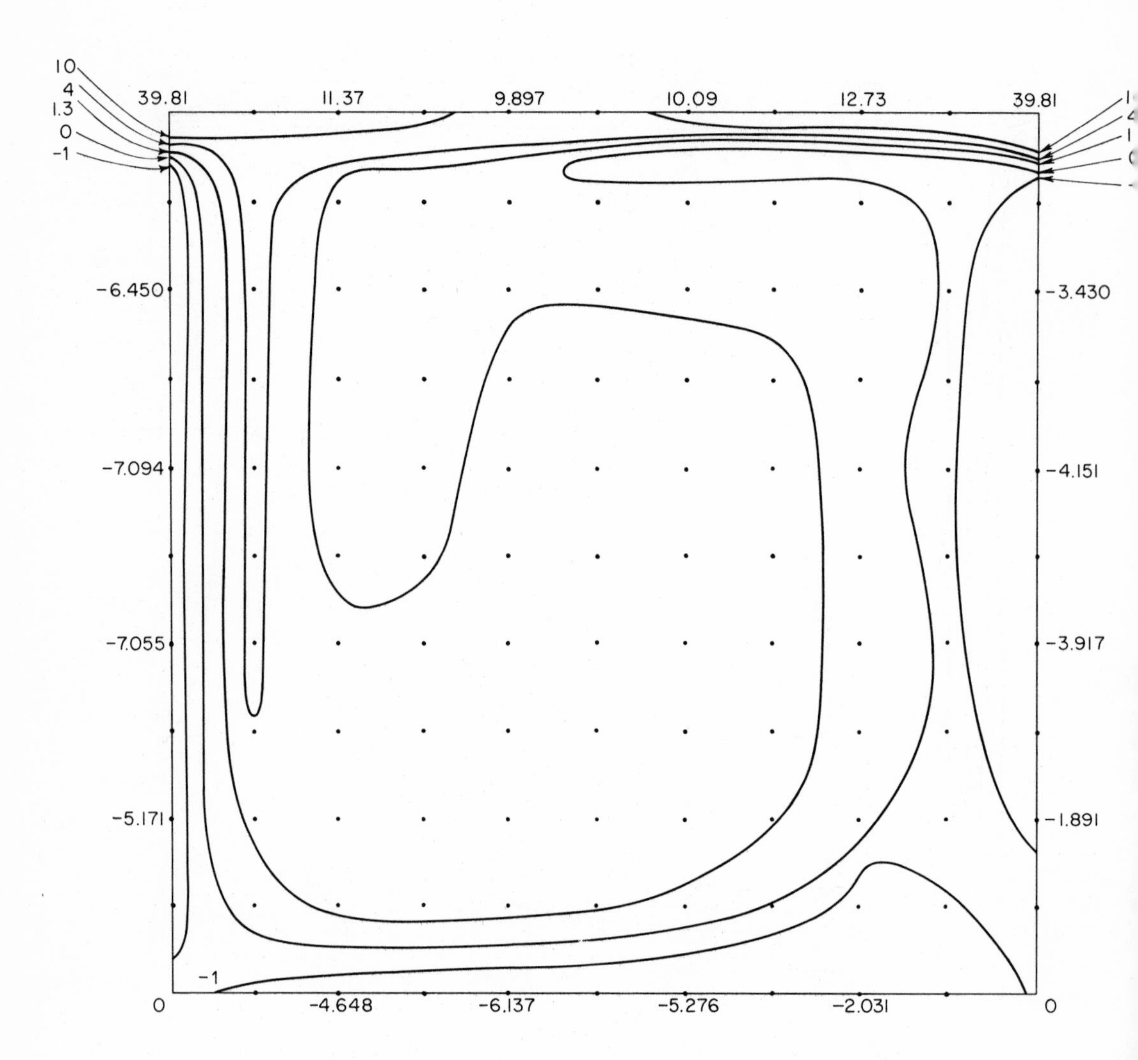

Figure 10.15. EQUIVORTICITY CURVES FOR REYNOLDS NUMBER 3000

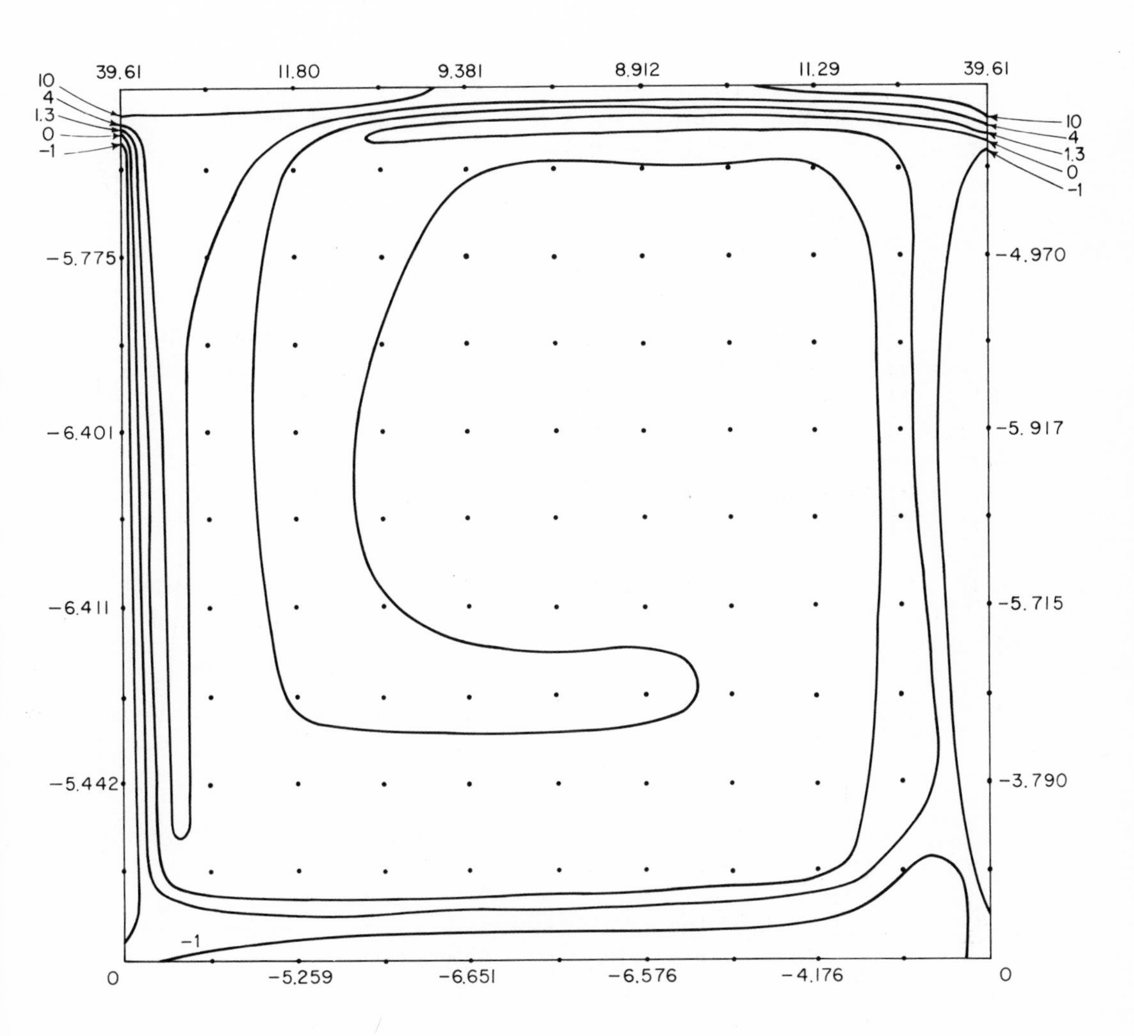

Figure 10.16. EQUIVORTICITY CURVES FOR REYNOLDS NUMBER 100,000

Bibliography

1. Ablow, C. M. and C. L. Perry, Iterative solutions of the Dirichlet problem for $\Delta u = u^2$. Jour. Soc. Indust. Appl. Math., vol. 7, no. 4, 1959, 459-467.

2. ________, Numerical solution of the Dirichlet problem for the quasilinear elliptic equation $\Delta u = buu$. Abstracts of Short Communications, I. C. M., Stockholm, 1962, 197.

3. Ageeva, Z. G. and V. K. Ivanov, On the numerical solution of the Cauchy problem for an equation of elliptic type (Russian). Ural. Gos. Univ. Mat. Zap. 4, 1964, 3-5.

4. Aizenstat, N. D., On an estimate of the error in approximate solution of a finite-difference Poisson equation (Russian). Mat. Sbornik N. S., 31(73), 1952, 485-490.

5. Akushsky, I., On numerical solution of the Dirichlet problem on punched-card machines (Russian). Bull. Acad. Sci. U. S. S. R., 54, 1946, 755-758.

6. Albrecht, R. F., Approximation to the solution of partial differential equations by the solutions of ordinary differential equations. Num. Mat., 2, 1960, 245-262.

7. Aleksidze, M. A., On the numerical solution of the Dirichlet problem for Poisson equations (Russian). Dokl. Akad. Nauk SSSR, 147, 1962, 1271-1273.

8. ________, A generalization of Gerschgorin's marjorantmethod (Russian). Trudy Vycisl. Centra Akad. Nauk Gruzin, SSR, 3, 1963.

9. ________, A remark on the majorant method of Batschelet (Russian). Soobsc. Akad. Nauk Gruzin, SSR, 34, 1964, 513-518.

10. Allen, D. N. de G. and S. C. R. Dennis, Graded nets in harmonic and biharmonic analysis. Quart. Jour. Mech. Appl. Math., 4, 1951, 439-443.

11. ________, The application of relaxation methods to the solution of differential equations in three dimensions, III. Three dimensional stress analysis. Quart. Jour. Mech. Appl. Math., 11, 1958, 172-184.

12. Allen, D. N. de G. and B. Robins, The application of relaxation methods to satisfy normal-gradient boundary conditions associated with three dimensional partial differential equations. Quart. Jour. Mech. Appl. Math., 15, 1962, 43-51.

13. Allen, D. N. de G. and R. T. Severn. The application of relaxation methods to the solution of non-elliptic partial differential equations. II. The solidification of liquids. Quart. Jour. Mech. Appl. Math., 5, 1952, 447-454.

14. Ames, W. F., Nonlinear partial differential equations in engineering. Academic Press, New York, 1965.

15. Amsden, A. A., The particle-in-cell method for the calculation of the dynamics of compressible fluids. Rpt. LA-3466, Los Alamos Scientific Laboratory, Los Alamos, N. M., 1966.

16. Arms, R. J. and L. D. Gates, Jr., The computation of an axially symmetric free boundary problem on NORC, part II. U. S. Naval Proving Ground Report 1533, Dahlgren, Va., 1957.

17. Badagadze, V. V., On the numerical solution of a second order equation of elliptic type (Russian). Soobsc. Akad. Nauk Gruzin, SSR, 30, 1963, 689-696.

18. ___________, Approximation of second order differential equations of elliptic type by difference equations (Russian). Soobsc. Akad. Nauk Gruzin. SSR, 31, 1963, 263-269.

19. ___________, Construction of difference schemes for a differential equation of the elliptic type of second order (Russian). Z. Vycisl. Mat. i Mat. Fiz., 6, 1966, 512-520.

20. Bahvalov, N. S., On a method for approximating solutions of Laplace's equation (Russian). Dokl. Akad. Nauk SSSR, (N. S.), 114, 1957, 455-458.

21. ___________, Numerical solution of the Dirichlet problem for Laplace's equation (Russian). Vestnik Moskov. Univ. Ser. Mat. Meh. Astr. Fiz. Him., no. 5, 1959, 171-195.

22. Batchelor, G. K., On steady laminar flow with closed streamlines at large Reynolds numbers. Jour. Fluid Mech., 1, 1956, 177-190.

23. Bateman, H., Irrotational motion of a compressible inviscid fluid. Proc. Nat. Acad. Sci., 16, 1930, 816-825.

24. Batschelet, E., Uber die numerische Auflosung von Randwertproblemen bei elliptischen partiellen Differentialgleichungen. ZAMP, 3, 1952, 165-193.

25. Becker, M., The principles and applications of variational methods. MIT Press, Cambridge, Mass., 1964.

26. Bellman, R., M. L. Juncosa, and R. Kalaba, Some numerical experiments using Newton's method for nonlinear parabolic and elliptic boundary-value problems. Comm. A. C. M., 4, 1961, 187-191.

27. Berger, J. M. and G. J. Lasher, The use of discrete Green's functions in the numerical solution of Poisson's equation. Ill. Jour. Math., vol. 2, no. 4A, 1958, 593-607.

28. Berger, M. S., A Sturm-Liouville theorem for nonlinear elliptic partial differential equations. Proc. Nat. Acad. Sci., 53, 1965, 1277-1280.

29. Bergman, S., A method for solving boundary value problems of mathematical physics on punch card machines. Jour. Assoc. Comp. Mach., 1, 1954, 101-104.

30. __________, Some methods for solutions of boundary-value problems of linear partial differential equations. Proc. Symp. Appl. Math. AMS, vol. 6, 1956, 11-29.

31. Bergman, S. and J. G. Herriot. Numerical solution of boundary value problems by the method of integral operators. Num. Mat., 7, 1965, 42-65.

32. Bernstein, D. L., Existence theorems in partial differential equations. Annals of Math. Studies, No. 23, Princeton University Press, Princeton, 1950.

33. Bernstein, F., Neuer Galton Apparat zur Durchfuhrung einer praktischen Losung der Randwertaufgaben der partiellen Differentialgleichungen $\Delta u = 0$ und $\Delta u = C$ mit besonderer Berucksichtigung des Torsionproblems. Zeits. f. Phys., 79, 1932, 684-695.

34. Bers, L., On mildly nonlinear partial difference equations of elliptic type. Jour. Res. Nat. Bur. Stand., vol. 51, no. 5, 1953, 229-236.

35. __________, Existence and uniqueness of a subsonic flow past a given profile. Comm. Pure Appl. Math., 7, 1954, 44-54.

36. Besicovitch, A. S., On the definition and value of the area of a surface. Quart. Jour. Math., 16, 1945, 86-102.

37. Bhargava, R. D. and H. C. Radhakrishna, Numerical solution of two-dimensional Laplace's equation. Proc. Nat. Inst. Sci. India, A, 29, 1963, 283-293.

38. Bickley, W. G., Finite difference formulas for the square lattice. Quart. Jour. Mech. Appl. Math. 1, 1948, 35-42.

39. Bickley, W. G., S. Michaelson, and M. R. Osborne, On finite-difference methods for the numerical solution of boundary-value problems. Proc. Roy. Soc. London A262, 1961, 219-236.

40. Birkhoff, G. and J. B. Diaz, Non-linear network problems. Quart. Appl. Math., 13, 1956, 431-443.

41. Bittner, E. C., Numerical analysis of Laplace's equation with nonlinear boundary conditions. Ph. D. thesis, Case Inst. Tech., 1965.

42. Boothroyd, A. R.; E. C. Cherry, R. Makar, An electrolytic tank for the measurement of steady state response, transient response and allied properties of networks. Proc. IEEE, 96, 1949, 163-177.

43. Bouwkamp, C. J., A simple method of calculating electrostatic capacity. Physica, 24, Zernike issue, 1958, 538-542.

44. Brakhage, H. and P. Werner, Über das Dirichletsche Aussenraumproblem für die Helmholtzsche Schwingungsgleichung. Archiv d. Math., 16, 1965, 325-329.

45. Bramble, J. H., Error estimates for difference methods in forced vibration problems. SIAM Jour. Num. Anal., 3, 1966, 1-12.

46. Bramble, J. H. and B. E. Hubbard, On the formulation of finite difference analogues of the Dirichlet problem for Poisson's equation. Num. Mat., 4, 1962, 313-327.

47. ___________, On a finite difference analogue of an elliptic boundary value problem which is neither diagonally dominant nor of non-negative type. Jour. Math. Phys., XLIII, 1964, 117-132.

48. ___________, New monotone type approximations for elliptic problems. Math. Comp., 18, 1964, 349-367.

49. Bramble, J. H. and B. E. Hubbard, Approximation of derivatives by finite difference methods in elliptic boundary value problems. In Contributions to Differential Equations, 3, 1964, 399-410.

50. __________, Approximation of solutions of mixed boundary value problems for Poisson's equation by finite differences. Jour. ACM, 12, 1965, 114-123.

51. Bramble, J. H. and L. E. Payne, Bounds for solutions of second order elliptic partial differential equations. Inst. Fluid Dyn. and Appl. Math., Tech. Note BN-237, College Park, Maryland, 1961.

52. Bruhn, G., Ein numerisches Verfahren zur Losung der Dirichletschen Randwertaufgabe fur ein System von zwei linearen elliptischen Differentialgleichungen. ZAMM, 44, 1964, 11-12.

53. Bruk, I. S., A mechanical device for the approximate solution of the Poisson-Laplace equations (Russian). Bull. Acad. Sci. U. S. S. R., 53, 1946, 311-312.

54. Burculadze, T. V., On an approximate solution of boundary value problems for a certain class of elliptic systems (Russian). Differencial'nye Uravnenija, 1, 1965, 1231-1245.

55. Burggraf, O. R., Analytical and numerical studies of the structure of separated flows, Jour. Fluid Mech., 24, 1966, 113-143.

56. Burgerhout, T. J., On the numerical solution of partial differential equations of elliptic type, I. Appl. Sci. Res., B4, 1954, 161-172.

57. Cannon, J. R., The numerical solution of the Dirichlet problem for Laplace's equation by linear programming. SIAM Jour., 12, 1964, 233-237.

58. Carre, B. A., The determination of the optimum accelerating factor for successive over-relaxation. Comp. Jour., 4, 1961, 73-78.

59. Chorin, A. J., The numerical solution of the Navier-Stokes equations for an incompressible fluid. AEC Report NYO-1480-82. Courant Institute of Mathematical Sciences, N. Y. U., 1967.

60. Chou, Yu-lin, Nonlinear partial differential equations, Chinese Mathematics, 2, 1962, 204-216.

61. Chow, T. S. and H. W. Milnes, Boundary contraction solution of Laplace's differential equation II. Jour. Assoc. Comp. Mach., vol. 7, no. 1, 1960, 37-45.

62. Chow, T. S. and H. W. Milnes, Numerical solution of the Neumann and mixed boundary value problems by boundary contraction. Jour Assoc. Comp. Mach., vol. 8, no. 3, 1961, 336-358.

63. __________, Solution of Laplace's equation by boundary contraction over regions of irregular shape. Num. Mat., 4, 1962, 209-225.

64. Churchill, R. V., Fourier series and boundary value problems. McGraw-Hill, New York, 1941.

65. Collatz, L., Bemerkungen zur Fehlerabschatzung fur das Differenzenverfahren bei partiellen Differentialgleichungen. ZAMM, 13, 1933, 56-57.

66. __________, Numerical treatment of differential equations. Springer, Berlin, 1960.

67. __________, Monotonic operators in numerical mathematics. Proc. Seventh Cong. Theor. Appl. Mech., Bombay, 1961, 253-258.

68. Comincioli, V., Analisi numerica di alcuni problemi ai limiti per l'operatore di Laplace iterato. Rend. Sem. Mat. Univ. Padova, 35, 1965, 190-235.

69. Concus, P., Numerical solution of the minimal surface equation. Math. Comp., 21, 1967, 340-350.

70. Conte, S. D. and R. T. Dames, An alternating direction method for solving the biharmonic equation. MTAC, 12, 1958, 198-205.

71. Cornock, A. F., The numerical solution of Poisson's and the biharmonic equations by matrices. Proc. Camb. Phil. Soc., 50, 1954, 524-535.

72. Courant, R., Dirichlet's principle, conformal mapping and minimal surfaces. Interscience, New York, 1950.

73. Courant, R., K. Friedrichs, and H. Lewy, Uber die partiellen Differenzengleichungen der mathematischen Physik. Math. Ann., 100, 1928, 32-74.

74. Courant, R. and D. Hilbert, Methods of mathematical physics, II. Interscience, New York, 1962.

75. Courant, R., E. Isaacson and M. Rees, On the solution of nonlinear hyperbolic differential equations by finite differences. Comm. Pure Appl. Math., 5, 1952, 243-255.

76. Crank, J. and P. Nicolson, A practical method for the numerical integration of solutions of partial differential equations of the heat conduction type. Proc. Camb. Phil. Soc., 43, 1947, 50-67.

77. Cryer, C. W., On the numerical solution of a quasi-linear elliptic equation. Jour. SIAM, 14, 1967, 363-375.

78. Curtiss, J. H., Solutions of the Dirichlet problem in the plane by approximation with Faber polynomials. SIAM Jour. Num. Anal., 3, 1966, 204-228.

79. Davidenko, D. F., On the solution of Laplace's equation with axial symmetry by a difference method (Russian). Dokl. Akad. Nauk SSSR, 114, 1957, 690-693.

80. __________, A difference method for the solution of the Poisson equation with axial symmetry (Russian). Dokl. Akad. Nauk SSSR, 118, 1958, 1066-1069.

81. __________, Solution by the method of nets of the axi-symmetric Dirichlet problem for the Laplace equation (Russian). Dokl. Akad. Nauk SSSR, 126, 1959, 471-473.

82. __________, Construction of difference equations for approximating the solution of the Euler-Poisson-Darboux equation (Russian). Dokl. Akad. Nauk SSSR, 142, 1962, 510-513.

83. Davidenko, D. F. and G. I. Biryuk, On the solution of Dirichlet's interval problem for Laplace's equation by the use of nets (Russian). Dokl. Akad. Nauk SSSR, 129, 1959, 246-249.

84. Davis, P. and P. Rabinowitz, Numerical experiments in potential theory using orthonormal functions, Jour. Wash. Acad. Sciences, 46, 1956, 12-17.

85. Deeter, C. R. and G. Springer, Discrete harmonic kernels. Jour. Math. and Mech., 14, 1965, 413-438.

86. Demjanovic, Ju. K., The method of nets for certain problems of mathematical physics. Soviet Math., 5, 1964, 1452-1456.

87. Diaz, J. B., Upper and lower bounds for quadratic integrals and, at a point, for solutions of linear boundary value problems. In _Boundary problems in differential equations_, Univ. Wisconsin Press, Madison, 1960, 47-83.

8. Diaz, J. B. and R. C. Roberts, Upper and lower bounds for the numerical solution of the Dirichlet difference boundary value problem. Jour. Math. Phys., 31, 1952, 184-191.

9. __________, On the numerical solution of the Dirichlet problem for Laplace's difference equation. Quart. Appl. Math., 9, 1952, 355-360.

0. Didenko, V. I. and I. N. Lyashenko, The numerical solution of boundary value problems for elliptic differential equations with constant coefficients (Russian). Ukr. Mat. Jour., 16, 1964, 681-690.

__________, On the numerical solution of boundary value problems for elliptic differential equations with constant coefficients. Dopovidi Akad. Nauk Ukrain., RSR, 10, 1964, 1273-1276.

2. DiPasquale, S., Generalization of the method of finite differences for the solution of equations with partial derivatives that can be reduced to a Laplace equation (Italian). G. Gen. Civ., 97, 1959, 486-497.

3. Doob, J. L., Discrete potential theory and boundaries. Jour. Math. Mech., vol. 8, no. 3, 1959, 433-458.

4. Douglas, Jesse, Solution of the Plateau problem. Trans. AMS, 33, 1931, 264.

5. Douglas, Jim, Jr., Alternating direction iteration for mildly nonlinear elliptic difference equations. Num. Mat., 3, 1961, 92-108.

6. __________, A correction to my paper "Alternating direction iteration for mildly nonlinear elliptic difference equations." Num. Mat., 4, 1962, 301-302.

7. __________, A survey of numerical methods for parabolic differential equations. In Advances in computers, II, Academic Press, New York, 1961, 1 - 55.

8. Dorny, C., Boundary approximations in the computer solution of Poisson's equation. Ph. D. thesis, Stanford, 1965.

9. Downing, A. C., Jr., On the convergence of steady state multiregion diffusion calculations. ORNL-2961, Oak Ridge National Laboratory, Oak Ridge, Tennessee, 1960.

0. Durand, E., L'approximation du sixieme ordre dans le calcul des solutions de l'equation de Poisson a trois variables. C. R. Acad. Sci. Paris, 245, 1957, 788-791.

101. Durand, E., Sur les solutions numeriques de l'equation de Poisson. Chiffres, 1, 1958, 3-16.

102. Dyson, J. D., Measuring the capacitance per unit length of two infinite cones of arbitrary cross section. Transactions, Professional Group on Antennas and Propagation, IRE, vol. AP 7, 1959, 102-103.

103. Edwards, T. E., Proton linear accelerator cavity calculations. MURA Rpt. 622, Off. Tech. Serv. U. S. Dept. Comm., 1961.

104. ________, Messymesh. MURA Rpt. 642, Off. Tech. Serv., U. S. Dept. Comm., 1962.

105. Ehrlich, L. W., Monte Carlo solutions of boundary value problems involving the difference analogue of $\frac{\partial^2 u}{\partial x^2} + \frac{\partial^2 u}{\partial y^2} + \frac{k}{y}\frac{\partial u}{\partial y} = 0$. Jour. Assoc. Comp. Mach., vol. 6, no. 2, 1959, 204-218.

106. Ehrlich, L. W., J. D. Riley, W. G. Strang, and B. A. Troesch, Finite-difference techniques for a boundary problem with an eigenvalue in a boundary condition. Jour. Soc. Industr. Appl. Math., vol. 9, no. 1, 1961, 149-164.

107. Eidus, D. M., On the solution of boundary value problems by the difference method (Russian). Dokl. Akad. Nauk SSSR, (N. S.), 83, 1952, 191-194.

108. ___________, On the solution of boundary problems by the method of finite differences (Russian). Dokl. Akad. Nauk SSSR, 83, 1953, 191-194.

109. Eisemann, K., Removal of ill-conditioning for matrices, Quart. Appl. Math., 15, 1957, 225-230.

110. Emmons, H. W., The numerical solution of partial differential equations. Quart. Appl. Math., 2, 1944, 173-195.

111. Engeli, M., Automatic treatment of elliptic boundary value problems. Schmidberger and Muller, Zurich, 1962.

112. Engeli, M, Th. Ginsburg, H. Rutishhauser, and E. Stiefel, Refined iterative methods for computation of the solution and the eigenvalues of self adjoint boundary value problems. Mitteilungen aus dem Institut fur angewandte Mathematik an der eidgenossischen technischen Hochschule in Zurich, No. 8, 1959.

3. Engeli, M. and P. Lauchli, Automatic calculation and programming of difference equations for elliptic boundary value problems. Proc. IFIPS Cong., Munich, 1962.

4. Evans, D. J., The solution of elliptic difference equations by stationary iterative processes. Proc. Int. Conf. Inf. Proc., Information Processing, Unesco, Paris, 1960, 79-85.

5. Eve, J. and H. I. Scoins, A note on the approximate solution of the equations of Poisson and Laplace by finite difference methods. Quart. Jour. Math. Oxford Ser., (2) 7, 1956, 217-223.

6. Euler, L., *Methodus inveniendi lineas curvas maximi minimive proprietate gaudentes.* M. Bousquet, Lausanne, 1744.

7. Fehlberg, E., Bemerkungen zur numerischen Behandlung des Dirichletschen Problems fur spezielle Rander. Acta Math., 87, 1952, 361-382.

8. __________, Bemerkungen zur numerischen Behandlung des Dirichletschen Problems fur allgemeine Rander. Acta Math., 91, 1954, 51-74.

9. Fichera, G., Sull'approssimazione delle funzioni armoniche in tre variabili mediante successioni di particolari funzioni armoniche. Rend. dell'Acc. Naz. Lincei, 1947.

0. __________, Formule di maggiorazione connesse ad una classe di transformazioni lineari. Ann. Mat. Pura Appl., 36, 1954, 273-296.

1. __________, Alcuni recenti sviluppi della teoria dei problemi al contorno per le equazioni alle derivate parziali lineari. Convegno Internazionale sulle Equazioni Lineari Alle Derivate Parziali, Trieste, 1954.

2. __________, Su un principio di dualita per talune formule di maggiorazione relative alle equazioni differenziali. Atti Accad. Naz. Lincei, 19, 1955, 411-418.

3. Finn, R., New estimates for equations of minimal surface type. Arch. Rat. Mech. Anal., 14, 1963.

4. Finn, R. and D. Gilbarg, Asymptotic behaviour and uniqueness of plane subsonic flows. Stanford Univ. Tech. Rpt. No. 225.

5. Forsythe, G. E., Solving linear algebraic equations can be interesting. Bull. AMS, 59, 1953, 299-329.

126. Forsythe, G. E., Difference methods on a digital computer for Laplacian boundary value and eigenvalue problems. Comm. Pure Appl. Math., 9, 1956, 425-434.

127. Forsythe, G. E. and T. S. Motzkin, An extension of Gauss' transformation for improving the condition of systems of linear equations. MTAC, 6, 1952, 9-17.

128. Forsythe, G. E. and W. Wasow, _Finite-difference methods for partial differential equations._ Wiley, New York, 1960.

129. Fox, L., Solution by relaxation methods of plane potential problems with mixed boundary conditions. Quart. Appl. Math., 2, 1944, 251-257.

130. __________, The numerical solution of elliptic differential equations when the boundary conditions involve a derivative. Phil. Trans. Roy. Soc. London, [A], 242, 1950, 345-378.

131. __________, _Numerical solution of ordinary and partial differential equations_. Addison-Wesley, Reading, Massachusetts, 1962.

132. Frank, T. G., Error bounds on numerical solutions of Dirichlet problems for quasilinear elliptic equations. Tech. Rpt. LA-3685, Los Alamos Sci. Lab., Los Alamos, N. M., 1967.

133. Frank, P. and R. von Mises, _Die Differential- und Integralgleichungen der Mechanik und Physik_, I, Rosenberg, New York, 2nd ed., 1943.

134. Frankel, S., Convergence rates of iterative treatments of partial differential equations. MTAC, 4, 1950, 65-75.

135. Franklin, J. N., _Conservative matrices in the numerical solution of elliptic partial differential equations_. Lecture notes, California Institute of Technology, 1959.

136. Frey, T. and P. Rozsa, Konvergenzschnelle des Differenzverfahrens der Poissonschen und der biharmonischen Differentialgleichungen, I. Period. Poly. Engrg., 4, 1960, 385-422.

137. Friedman, A., _Partial differential equations of parabolic type_. Prentice Hall, New Jersey, 1964.

138. Friedman, B., The iterative solution of elliptic difference equations. Report NYO-7698. A. E. C. Computing Facility, New York University, 1957.

39. Friedman, H. A., S. F. Persselin, B. L. McFarland, J. D. Leader, Effect of rocket engine combustion on chamber materials. Part II: Two dimensional computer program. Rpt. AFRPL-TR-65-176, Rocket Propulsion Lab., Edwards, California, 1965.

40. Friedrichs, K. O., A finite difference scheme for the Neumann and the Dirichlet problem. Report NYO-9760, A. E. C. Computing Center, New York University, 1962.

41. Friis, H. T. and S. A. Schelkunoff, Antennas: theory and practice. John Wiley, New York, 1952.

42. Frocht, M. M., The numerical solution of Laplace's equation in composite rectangular areas. Jour. Appl. Phys., 17, 1946, 730-742.

43. Frocht, M. M. and M. M. Leven, A rational approach to the numerical solution of Laplace's equation. Jour. Appl. Phys., 12, 1941, 596-604.

44. Fromm, J. E. and F. H. Harlow, Numerical solution of the problem of vortex street development. Phys. of Fluids, 6, 1963, 975-985.

45. Gagua, M., On approximate solution of linear boundary problems for elliptic equations (Russian). Dokl. Akad. Nauk SSSR(N. S.), 102, 1955, 1061-1064.

46. Garabedian, P. R., Estimation of the relaxation factor for small mesh size. MTAC, 10, 1956, 183-185.

47. ___________, Applicazione al flurso supersonico del problema di Cauchy per un'equazione ellitica. Atti Accad. Naz. Lincei Rend. Cl. Sci. Fis. Mat. Nat., (8) 24, 1958, 282-286.

48. Garza, A. de la, Error bounds for a numerical solution of a recurring linear system. Quart. Appl. Math., 13, 1956, 453-456.

49. Gatun, V. P., On the numerical solution of three dimensional boundary value problems in potential theory by the superposition of representations (Russian). In Approximate methods of solving differential equations, Izdat. Akad. Nauk Ukrain. SSR, Kiev, 1963, 19-26.

50. Gelfand, I. M. and S. V. Fomin, Calculus of variations. Prentice Hall, Englewood Cliffs, N. J., 1963.

51. Gerschgorin, S., On the approximate integration of the Laplace and Poisson differential equations (Russian). Ann. Poly. Inst. Leningrad, 30, 1927.

152. Gerschgorin, S., Fehlerabschatzung fur das Differenzenverfahren sur Lösung partieller Differentialgleichungen. ZAMM, 10, 1930, 373-382.

153. Giese, J. H., On the truncation error in a numerical solution of the Neumann problem for a rectangle. Jour. Math. Phys., vol. 37, no. 2, 1958, 169-177.

154. Ghelardoni, G., Sopra un nuovo procedimento per lu valuatzione dell'errore nella soluzione del problema di Dirichlet sul rettangolo con i metodi alle differenze e con l'uso di un calcolatore elettronico. Atti. Sem. mat. fis. Univ. Modena, 10, 1961, 197-218.

155. Giraud, G., Sur certains problemes non lineaires de Neumann et sur certains problemes non lineaires mixtes. Ann. Ec. N. Sup., 49, 1932, 1-104, 245-308.

156. __________, Problemes des types de Dirichlet et de Neumann dans certains cas ou les donnees sont discontinues. C. R. Ac. Sc. Paris, 201, 1935, 925-928.

157. __________, Nouvelle methode pour traiter certains problemes relatifs aux equations du type elliptique. Jour. de Math., 18, 1939, 111-143.

158. Goldstine, H. H. and J. von Neumann, Numerical inverting of matrices of high order, II. Proc. AMS, 2, 1951, 188-202.

159. Goodwin, E. T. (editor), Modern computing methods. Philosophical Library, New York, 2nd ed., 1961.

160. Greenspan, D., On evaluating the Stokes stream function by means of a symmetric difference analogue. Riv. Mat. Univ. Parma, 9, 1958, 87-93.

161. ________, On a nine point method for the numerical evaluation of the Stokes stream function. Port. Mat., 17, 1958, 97-106.

162. ________, On the numerical solution of n-dimensional boundary value problems associated with Poisson's equation. Jour. Frank. Inst., 226, 1958, 365-371.

163. ________, Note on difference equation approximations of Laplace's equation. Jour. Frank. Inst., 268, 1959, 46-52.

164. ________, On the numerical solution of Dirichlet-type problems. Amer. Math. Mo., 66, 1959, 40-46.

65. Greenspan, D., *Introduction to partial differential equations*. McGraw-Hill, New York, 1961.

66. ________, On the approximate solution of a class of strongly elliptic linear differential equations. Jour. Frank. Inst., 271, 1961, 471-487.

67. ________, On the numerical solution of problems allowing mixed boundary conditions. Jour. Frank. Inst., 277, 1964, 11-30.

68. ________, Partial difference approximations with non-negative coefficients. Jour. Frank. Inst., 275, 1963, 481-490.

69. ________, The approximate solution of axially symmetric problems. Comm. ACM, 7, 1964, 373-377.

70. ________, Recent computational results in the numerical solution of elliptic boundary value problems. Tech. Rpt. 408, Math. Res. Ctr., Madison, Wisconsin, 1963.

71. ________, *Introductory numerical analysis of elliptic boundary value problems.* Harper and Row, New York, 1965.

72. ________, On approximating extremals of functionals. Part I. The method and examples for boundary value problems. Bull. ICC, Univ. Rome, 4, 1965, 99-120.

73. ________, Resolution of classical capacity problems by means of a digital computer. Can. Jour. Phys., 44, 1966, 2605-2613.

74. ________, On approximating extremals of functionals. Part II. Theory and generalizations related to boundary value problems for nonlinear differential equations. Int. Jour. Eng. Sci., 5, 1967, 571-588.

75. ________, Approximate solution of initial-boundary wave equation problems by boundary value techniques. Tech. Rpt. #778, Math. Res. Ctr., U. Wisconsin, Madison, 1967.

76. ________, Approximate solution of initial-boundary parabolic problems by boundary value techniques. Tech. Rpt. #782, Math. Res. Ctr., U. Wisconsin, Madison, 1967.

77. ________, A numerical approach to biharmonic problems. Comp. Jour., 10, 1967, 198-201.

78. ________, Numerical studies of two dimensional, steady state Navier-Stokes equations for arbitrary Reynolds number. Tech. Rpt. #9, Dept. of Computer Sciences, U. Wisconsin, Madison, 1967.

179. Greenspan, D., Numerical studies of viscous, incompressible flow through an orifice for arbitrary Reynolds number. Tech. Rpt. #20, Dept. Computer Sciences, U. Wisconsin, Madison, 1968.

180. Greenspan, D. and P. C. Jain, Numerical study of subsonic fluid flow by a combination variational integral - finite difference technique. Jour. Math. Anal. Appl., 18, 1967, 85-111.

181. Greenspan, D. and E. Silverman, The calculation of electrostatic capacity by means of a high speed digital computer. Proc. IEEE, 53, 1965, 1636.

182. Greenspan, D. and S. V. Parter, Mildly nonlinear elliptic partial differential equations and their numerical solution. II. Num. Mat., 7, 1965, 129-146.

183. Greenspan, D. and R. Warten, On the approximate solution of Dirichlet-type problems with singularities on the boundary. Jour. Frank. Inst., 273, 1962, 187-200.

184. Greenspan, D. and P. Werner, A numerical method for the exterior Dirichlet problem for the reduced wave equation. Arch. Rat. Mech. Anal., 23, 1966, 288-316.

185. Greenspan, D. and M. Yohe, On the approximate solution of $\Delta u = F(u)$. Comm. ACM, 6, 1963, 564-568.

186. Griffin, D. S. and R. S. Varga, Numerical solution of plane elasticity problems. Jour. SIAM, 11, 1963, 1046-1062.

187. Grohne, D., Uber die numerische Anwendbarkeit der Parametrixmethode bei partiellen Differentialgleichungen. Rpt. #33, Max-Plank-Inst., Gottingen, 1965.

188. Grunsch, H. J., Eine Fehlerabschatzung bei der dritten Randwertaufgabe der Potentialtheorie. ZAMM, 32, 1952, 279-281.

189. Gunn, J. E., The numerical solution of $\nabla \cdot a \nabla u = f$ by a semi-explicit alternating-direction iterative technique. Num. Mat., 6, 1964, 181-184.

190. ________, On the two-stage iterative method of Douglas for mildly nonlinear elliptic difference equations. Num. Mat., 6, 1964, 243-249.

191. Hajdin, N., Ein Verfahren zur numerischen Lösung der Randwertaufgaben vom elliptischen Typus. Acad. Serbe Sci., Publ. Inst. Mat., 9, 1956, 69-78.

92. Hartee, D. R., Numerical analysis. Clarendon Press, Oxford, England, 1952.

93. Heilbronn, H., On discrete harmonic functions, Proc. Camb. Phil. Soc., 45, 1949, 194-206.

94. Herriot, J. G., Inequalities for the capacity of a lens. Duke Math. Jour., 15, 1948, 743-753.

95. Higgins, T. J. and D. K. Reitan. Calculation of electrical capacitance of a cube. Jour. Appl. Phys., 22, 1951, 223-226.

96. Hills, N. L., A priori estimate of the discretization error of some discrete Laplacian operators. Abstract 636-122, Notices of AMS, 13, 1966, 612-613.

97. Hirschfelder, J. O., G. F. Curtiss and R. B. Bird, Molecular theory of gases and liquids. Wiley, N. Y., 1954.

98. Ho Yu-kung, On the convergence and finiteness of variance of some Monte Carlo methods for solving elliptic partial differential eqations (Chinese). Jour. Tsing Hua Univ., 11, 1964, 109-128.

99. Hochstrasser, U. W., Numerical experiments in potential theory using the Nehari estimates. MTAC, 12, 1958, 26-33.

200. Hockney, R. W., A past direct solution of Poisson's equation using Fourier analysis. Report CS6, Stanford Univ., 1964.

201. Hofmann, P., Asymptotic expansions of the discretization error of boundary value problems of the Laplace equation in rectangular domains. Num. Mat., 9, 1967, 302-322.

202. Hopf, E., The partial differential equation $u_t + uu_x = \mu u_{xx}$. Comm. Pure Appl. Math., 3, 1950, 201-230.

203. Howland, J. L., The numerical solution of an induced potential problem. Jour. Math. Anal. Appl., 8, 1964, 245-257.

204. Hubbard, B. and J. Bramble. A priori bounds on the discretization error in the numerical solution of the Dirichlet problem. In Contributions to differential equations, II, 1963, 229-252.

205. Huber, A., On the uniqueness of generalized axially symmetric potentials. Ann. Math., 60, 1954, 351-358.

206. Huber, A., Some results on generalized axially symmetric potentials. Proc. Conf. Diff. Equations, College Park, Maryland, 1955, 147-155.

207. Hyman, M. A., Non-iterative numerical solution of boundary value problems. Appl. Sci. Res., B2, 1952, 325-351.

208. ________, On the numerical solution of partial differential equations. Thesis, Tech. Hogeschool, Delft, 1953.

209. Imai, I., On the flow of a compressible fluid past a circular cylinder. Proc. Phys.-Math. Soc. Japan, 23, 1941, 180-193.

210. Inerbaev, M. S., On the errors in finite difference solutions of second and third boundary value problems for elliptic eqations (Russian). Metody Vycisl, 2, 1963, 50-59.

211. ________, Some remarks on the work of Bers (Russian). In _Studies in differential equations and their applications_ (Russian), Izdat. "Nauka", Alma-Ata, 1965, 121-125.

212. Inoue, M., Discrete Neumann problem. Jour. Inst. Poly. Osaka City Univ., Ser. A5, 1954, 101-109.

213. Jackson, D., _Fourier series and orthogonal polynomials_. Carus Monograph 6, Math. Assoc. Amer., 1941.

214. Jain, M. K., Collocation method for physical problems. Thesis for the D. Sc., Indian Institute of Technology, Kharagpur, 1963.

215. Jain, M. K. and M. M. Chawla, Convergence of the collocation method over rectangular domains with estimates for the error norm. Research Rpt. # 11, Indian Inst. Tech., New Delhi, 1966.

216. Jamet, P. and S. V. Parter, Numerical methods for elliptic differential equations whose coefficients are singular on a portion of the boundary. SIAM Jour. Num. Anal., 4, 1967, 131-146.

217. John, F., _Partial differential equations._ Lecture notes, New York University, 1952-1953.

218. ________, _Advanced numerical analysis_. Lecture notes, New York University, 1956.

219. ________, On integration of parabolic equations by difference methods. Comm. Pure Appl. Math., 5, 1952, 155-211.

220. Kalaba, R., On nonlinear differential equations, the maximum operation, and monotone convergence. Jour. Math. Mech., 8, 1959, 519-574.

221. Karimberdieva, S., An error bound for the solution of Poisson's equation by various methods (Russian). Izv. Akad. Nauk U_ZSSR Ser. Fiz-Mat. Nauk, no. 6, 1963, 7-13.

222. Kantorovich, L. and V. Krylov, Approximate methods in higher analysis. Noordhoff, Amsterdam, Netherlands, 1958.

223. Karlquist, O., Numerical solution of elliptic difference equations by matrix methods, Tellus, 4, 1959, 374-384.

224. Karpenko, P. D., On a numerical method of mapping a polygon onto a circle (Ukranian). Dopovidi Akad. Nauk Ukrain RSR, 1964, 177-180.

225. Keller, H. B., Special block iterations with applications to Laplace and biharmonic difference equations. SIAM Rev., 2, 1960, 277-287.

226. Kellogg, O. D., Foundations of potential theory. Unger, N. Y., 1929.

227. Kellogg, R. B., An error estimate for elliptic difference equations on a convex polygon. SIAM Jour. Num. Anal., 3, 1966, 79-90.

228. Kelman, R. B., Axisymmetrical potential problems suggested by biological considerations. Bull. AMS, 69, 1963, 835-838.

229. Klabukova, L. S., Approximate method of solution for the problems of Hilbert and Poincare (Russian). Vycisl. Mat., 3, 1958, 34-87.

230. Kleiner, W., Sur les approximations de M. Leja dans le probleme plan de Dirichlet. Ann. Polon. Math., 15, 1964, 203-209.

231. Kline, M. and I. W. Kay, Electromagnetic theory and geometrical optics. Interscience, N. Y., 1965.

232. Kliot-Dasinskii, M. I., On a method of solution of a plane problem in potential theory (Russian). Leningrad Inzen.-Stroit. Inst. Sb. Nauk Trudov, 17, 1954, 11-27.

233. Korolyuk, V. S., On a method of increasing the asymptotic accuracy of the method of grids (Russian). Dokl. Akad. Nauk SSSR, (N. S.) 101, 1955, 985-987.

234. Krasnoselskii, M. A., Positive solutions of operator equations. Noordhoff, Groningen, 1964.

235. Kreiss, H. O., Difference approximations for the initial-boundary value problem for hyperbolic differential equations. In Numerical solutions of nonlinear differential equations, Wiley, N.Y., 1966, 141-166.

236. Krylov, N. and N. Bogoliubov, Application de la methode de l'algorithme variationnel a la solution approchee des equations differentielles aux derivees partielles du type elliptique, I, II. Bull. Acad. Sci. Leningrad, 1930, 43-71, 105-114.

237. Kucerenko, E. I., On the convergence of Galerkin's method for non-linear harmonic equations (Russian). Kazan State Univ., 1962, Sci. Survey Conf., Izdat. Kazan Univ., Kazan, 1963, 52-53.

238. Kunin, I. A., Approximate method of solution of boundary value problems for certain equations of elliptic type (Russian). Izv. Akad. Nauk SSSR, Otd. Tekh. Nauk, no. 10, 1958, 146-149.

239. Laasonen, P., On the degree of convergence of discrete approximations for the solutions of the Dirichlet problem. Ann. Acad. Sci. Fenn. A.I., 246, 1957, 1-19.

240. ________, On the truncation error of discrete approximations to the solutions of Dirichlet problems in a domain with corners. Jour. Assoc. Comp. Mach., vol. 5, no. 1, 1958, 32-38.

241. ________, On the solution of Poisson's difference equation. Jour. Assoc. Comp. Mach., 5, 1958, 370-382.

242. Ladyzenskaya, O. A., The method of finite differences in the theory of partial differential equations. AMS Translations, series 2, vol. 20, 1962, 77-104.

243. Laing, E. W., S. J. Roberts and R. T. P. Whipple, Equilibrium configurations of a toroidal plasma. Jour. Nuclear Energy, Part C, Plasma Physics, 1, 1959, 49-54.

244. Landau, H. G., A simple procedure for improved accuracy in the resistor-network solution of Laplace's and Poisson's equations. Jour. Appl. Mech., March, 1957, 93-97.

245. Langer, R. E. (editor), Partial differential equations and continuum mechanics. Univ. Wisconsin Press, Madison, Wisconsin, 1961.

246. Lapuskin, I. T., Concerning the solution of difference approximations of biharmonic equations by the method of successive approximations (Russian). Ukrain. Mat. Z., 12, 1960, 346-349.

247. Lebedev, V. I., The finite difference analogue of Neumann's problem (Russian). Doklady Akad. Nauk SSSR, 126, 1959, 494-497.

248. ________, The method of nets in the second boundary value problem for Poisson's equation (Russian). Doklady Akad. Nauk SSSR, 127, 1959, 742-745.

249. ________, Dirichlet's and Neumann's problems on triangular and hexagonal lattices. Soviet Math., 2, 1961, 519-522.

250. ________, Four-point schemes of increased accuracy (Russian). Dokl. Akad. Nauk SSSR, 142, 1962, 526-529.

251. ________, The solution of the Neumann problem by the method of nets (Russian). Vopr. vychisl. matem. i vychisl. tekhn. M., Mashgiz, 1963, 94-98.

252. ________, Difference analogues of orthogonal decomposition, fundamental differential operators, and certain boundary value problems of mathematical physics (Russian). Z. Vycisl. Mat. i Mat. Fiz., 4, 1964, 449-465 (part I), 649-659 (part II).

253. Lees, M., Approximate solution of parabolic problems. Jour. SIAM, 7, 1959, 167-183.

254. ________, Energy inequalities for the solution of differential equations. Trans. AMS, 94, 1960, 58-73.

255. ________, Alternating direction methods for hyperbolic differential equations. Jour. SIAM, 10, 1962, 610-616.

256. Le Roux, J., Sur le probleme de Dirichlet. Jour. Math., 10, 1964, 189-230.

257. Lesky, P., Calcolo numerico: Ricerca di una funzione armonica soggetta a condizioni al contorno non lineari. Rend. Accad. Sci. Fis. Mat. Napoli, (4) 19, 1953, 145-149.

258. Levinson, N., Dirichlet problem for $\Delta u = f(P, u)$. Jour. Math. Mech., 12, 1963, 567-576.

259. Lichtenstein, L., Randwertaufgaben der Theorie der linearen partiellen Differentialgleichungen zweiter Ordnung vom elliptischen Typus, II. Jour. fur Math., 143, 1913, 51-105.

260. Lichtenstein, L., Neuere Entwicklung der Theorie partial Differentialgleichungen zweiter Ordnung vom elliptischen Typus. Enzyklopadie der mathematischen Wissenschaften, 2, part 3, Teubner, Leipzig, 1923-1927, 1303-1305.

261. Lieberstein, H. M., A numerical test case for the nonlinear overrelaxation algorithm. Tech. Rpt. 122, Math. Res. Ctr., Madison, Wisconsin, 1960.

262. ________, A continuous method in numerical analysis applied to examples from a new class of boundary value problems. Tech. Rpt. 175, Math. Res. Ctr., Madison, Wisconsin, 1960.

263. Liebmann, H., Die angenahrte Ermittling harmonischer Funktionen und konformer Abbildungen. Sitz-Ber. boyr. Akad. Wiss. Munchen, math.-phys. Klasse, 1918, 385-416.

264. Littman, W., Finite difference methods for elliptic equations of arbitrary order. Notices of AMS, Abstract 546-67, 1958.

265. Loh, S. C., The calculation of the electric potential and the capacity of a tore by means of toroidal functions. Can. Jour. Phys., 37, 1959, 698-702.

266. Lucka, A. Ju., Application of the method of Ju. D. Sokolov to the solution of the exterior Neumann problem for the Poisson equation (Ukranian). Dopovidi Akad. Nauk Ukrain. RSR, 1965, 547-550.

267. Lush, P. E. and T. M. Cherry, The variational method in hydrodynamics. QJMAM, 9, 1956, 6-21.

268. Lynch, R. E., Error bound on a numerical solution of the quasi-linear wave equation. Ph. D. thesis, Harvard, Cambridge, Mass., 1963.

269. Lynch, R. E., J. R. Rice and D. H. Thomas, Direct solution of partial difference equations by tensor product methods. Num. Mat., 3, 1964, 185-199.

270. Lyusternik, L. A., On general network approximations of the Laplace operator (Russian). Dokl. Akad. Nauk SSSR (N. S.), 91, 1953, 1267-1269.

271. ________, On difference approximations of the Laplace operator (Russian). Uspehi Mat. Nauk (N. S.), 9, no. 2 (60), 1954, 3-66.

272. ________, A difference analogue of Green's function in three space (Russian). Vycislit Mat., 1, 1957, 3-22.

273. MacNeal, R. H., An asymmetrical finite difference network. Quart. Appl. Math., 11, 295-310.

274. Maergoiz, I. D., Error estimation in the numerical solution of boundary value problems for certain elliptic equations by the net method. USSR Comp. Math. and Math. Phys., 5, 1965, 268-272.

275. Maiorov, I. V., Approximate solutions of equations of elliptic type (Russian). Izv. Vyss. Ucebn. Zaved. Mat., no. 3(4), 1958, 160-162.

276. Mangasarian, O. L., Numerical solution of the first biharmonic problem by linear programming. Int. Jour. Eng. Sci., 1, 1963, 231-240.

277. Matheson, J. E. and D. G. Luenberger, Magnetic structure design aided by a digital computer. Research Rpt. 64-1D3-295-R1, Westinghouse Res. Lab., Pitts., Pa., 1964.

278. McAllister, G. T., Some nonlinear elliptic partial differential equations and difference equations. Jour. SIAM, 12, 1964, 772-777.

279. ________, An ordinate-uniqueness theorem for the Dirichlet problem for the system $\Delta u = v^2$, $\Delta v = u^2$. Jour. Math. Anal. Appl., 14, 1966, 297-300.

280. ________, Difference methods for a nonlinear elliptic system of partial differential equations. Quart. Appl. Math., 23, 1966, 355-359.

281. ________, Quasilinear uniformly elliptic partial differential equations and difference equations. SIAM Jour. Num. Anal., 3, 1966, 13-33.

282. McDowell, L. K., Variable successive over-relaxation. Rpt. 244, Dept. Comp. Sci., Univ. Illinois, Urbana, 1967.

283. Mikeladze, S. E., On the numerical solution of the equations of Laplace and Poisson (Russian). Izv. Akad. Nauk SSSR, Ser. Math. no. 2, 1938, 271-290.

284. ________, On the integration of differential equations by the difference method (Russian). Izv. Akad. Nauk SSSR, Ser. Math., 1939, 627-642.

285. ________, On the question of numerical integration of partial differential equations by means of nets (Russian). Mitt. Georg. Abt. Akad. Wiss. USSR, 1, 1940, 249-254.

286. ________, On the solution of boundary value problems by the difference method (Russian). C. R. (Doklady)Acad. Sci. USSR, (N. S.) 28, 1940, 400-402.

287 Mikeladze, S. E., Numerical integration of equations of elliptic and parabolic type (Russian). Izv. Akad. Nauk SSSR, 5, 1941, 57-74.

288. Miller, C. K., Three circle theorems in partial differential equations and applications to improperly posed problems. Ph. D. thesis, Rice Univ., Houston, 1963.

289. Milne, W. E., Numerical calculus. Princeton Univ. Press, Princeton, 1950.

290. ________, Numerical methods associated with Laplace's equation. Proceedings of the Second Symposium on Large Scale Digital Calculating Machines, Harvard Univ. Press, Cambridge, Mass., 1951, 152-163.

291. ________, Numerical solution of differential equations. Wiley, New York, 1953.

292. Milnes, H. W. and R. B. Potts, Numerical solution of partial differential equations by boundary contraction. Quart. Appl. Math., vol. 18, no. 1, 1960, 1-13.

293. Miracle, C. L., Approximate solutions of the telegrapher's equation by difference-equation methods. Jour. SIAM, 10, 1962, 517-527.

294. Miranda, C., Approssimazione di una funzione armonica in tre variabili mediante polinomii armonici. Rend. Circ. Mat. Palermo, 1932.

295. ________, Sull'approssimazione delle funzioni armoniche in tre variabili. Rend. Acc. Naz. Lincei, 1948.

296. ________, Equazioni alle derivate parziali di tipo ellitico. Springer, Berlin, 1955.

297. Miyakoda, K., Numerical calculations of Laplacian and Jacobian using 9 and 25 gridpoint systems. Jour. Meteorol. Soc. Japan (II), 38, 1960, 94-106.

298. ________, Test of convergence speed of iterative methods for solving 2- and 3-dimensional elliptic-type differential equations. Jour. Meteorol. Soc. Japan, (II), 38, 1960, 107-124.

299. Molchanov, I. M., On a space-saving storage method for the solution of Poisson's equation (Ukranian). Dopovidi Akad. Nauk Ukrain, RSR, 1962, 443-447.

300. Molchanov, I. M., Several methods for solving elliptic differential equations on digital computers (Ukranian). Dopovidi AN URSR, 1, 1963, 3-6.

301. ________, On methods of saving digital computer storage in the solution of difference equations (Russian). Sibirsk. Mat. Zh., 5, 1964, 109-123.

302. Moler, C. B., Finite difference methods for the eigenvalues of Laplace's operator. Tech. Rpt. CS22, Stanford Univ., 1965.

303. Morawetz, C. S., The decay of solutions of the exterior initial-boundary value problem for the wave equation, Comm. Pure Appl. Math., 14, 1961, 561-568.

304. Morrey, C. B., Multiple integral problems in the calculus of variations. Univ. Cal. Press, Berkeley, 1943.

305. Morse, P. M. and H. Fishbach, Methods of mathematical physics. II. McGraw-Hill, New York, 1953.

306. Moskovitz, D., The numerical solution of Laplace's and Poisson's equations. Quart. Appl. Math., 2, 1944, 148-163.

307. Motzkin, T. S. and W. Wasow, On the approximation of linear elliptic partial differential equations with positive coefficients. Jour. Math. Phys., 31, 1953, 253-259.

308. Mozok, G. M., On the solution of a class of problems of mathematical physics by the method of nets (Ukranian). Dopovidi Akad. Nauk RSR, 1963, 1570-1573.

309. ________, Stable computing algorithms for the solution of equations of elliptic type with variable coefficients (Ukranian). Visnik Kiev Univ., 6, 1964, 102-107.

310. ________, On solving biharmonic problems by the method of nets (Ukranian). Dopovidi Akad. Nauk RSR, 1964, 163-166.

311. Muller, M. E., On discrete operators connected with the Dirichlet problem. Jour. Math. Phys., 35, 1956, 89-113.

312. Myerott, R. E., P. J. Luke, W. W. Clendenin, and S. Geltman, A numerical variational method. Phys. Review, II., series 85, 1952, 393-400.

313. Mysovskih, I. P., Application of Caplygin's method to the solution of the Dirichlet problem for a special type of elliptic differential equation (Russian). Dokl. Akad. Nauk SSSR (N. S.), 99, 1954, 13-15.

314. ________, On a boundary problem for the equation $\Delta u = k(x,y)u^2$ (Russian). DAN, 94, 1954, 995-998.

315. Nehari, Z., Conformal mapping. McGraw-Hill, New York, 1952.

316. ________, On the numerical solution of the Dirichlet problem. Proc. Conf. Diff. Equations, College Park, Maryland, 1956, 157-178.

317. Newman, D. J., Numerical solution of a Cauchy problem for elliptic partial differential equations. AVCO Manuf. Corp, Lawrence, Massachusetts, 1957.

318. Nirenberg, L., Existence theorems in partial differential equations. Unpublished lecture notes, New York University.

319. ________, On elliptic partial differential equations. Ann. Scuola Norm. Sup. Pisa, series III, vol. 13, 1959, 1-48.

320. Nitsche, J. C. C., On new results in the theory of minimal surfaces. Bull. AMS, 71, 1965, 195-270.

321. Nitsche, J. and J. C. C. Nitsche, Error estimates for the numerical solution of elliptic differential equations. Arch. Rat. Mech. and Anal., 5, 1960, 293-306.

322. Nitsche, J. C. C. and J. Nitsche, Fehlerabschatzung fur die numerische Berechnung von Integralen, die Lösungen elliptischer Differentialgleichungen enthalten. Arch. Rat. Mech. Anal., vol. 5, no. 4, 1960, 307-314.

323. Noble, B., Variational principles in compressible fluid flow. Lecture notes, Applied Math. Sem., Math. Res. Ctr., U. Wisconsin, Madison, 1965.

324. O'Brien, G. G., M. A. Hyman, and S. Kaplan, A study of the numerical solution of partial differential equations. Jour. Math. Phys., 29, 1951, 223-251.

325. Omarov, E. O., An approximate solution by the method of lines of an elliptic partial differential equation of type 1 (Russian). Z. Vycisl. Mat. i Mat. Fiz., 4, 1964, 585-592.

326. Ortega, J. M. and W. C. Rheinboldt, Monotone iterations for nonlinear equations with application to Gauss-Seidel methods. Tech. Rpt. 66-32, Comp. Sci. Center, U. Md., Coll. Pk., 1966.

327. Oretga, J. M. and M. L. Rockoff, Nonlinear difference equations and Gauss-Seidel type iterative methods. Tech. Rpt. 65-20, Comp. Sci. Center, U. Md., Coll. Pk., 1965.

328. Ostrowski, A. M., Solution of Equations and Systems of Equations, Second Edition, Academic Press, New York, 1966.

329. Panov, D. J., An approximate graphical solution of the boundary problems of Laplace's equation (Russian). Trans. Center Aero-Hydro. Inst., nr. 169, 1934, 3-24.

330. ________, The numerical solution of boundary value problems of partial differential equations of elliptic type (Russian). Uspekhi Matem. Nauk, 4, 1938, 34-44.

331. Parr, W. E., Upper and lower bounds for the capacitance of the regular solids. Jour. SIAM, 9, 1961, 334-386.

332. Parter, S. V., Some computational results on "two-line" iterative methods for the biharmonic difference equation. Jour. Assoc. Comp. Mach., 8, 1961, 359-365.

333. ________, On estimating the "rates of convergence" of iterative methods for elliptic difference equations. Tech. Rpt. 28, Appl. Math. and Stat. Labs., Stanford Univ., Palo Alto, California, 1963.

334. ________, Mildly nonlinear elliptic partial differential equations and their numerical solution. I. Num. Math., 7, 1965, 113-128.

335. ________, On the existence and uniqueness of symmetric axially symmetric potentials. Arch. Rat. Mech. Anal., 20, 1965, 279-286.

336. ________, Numerical methods for generalized axially symmetric potentials. Jour. SIAM Num. Anal., 2, 1965, 500-515.

337. ________, Remarks on the numerical computation of solutions of $\Delta u = f(P, u)$. In Numerical solution of partial differential equations, Academic Press, N. Y., 1966, 73-82.

338. Payne, L. E. and H. F. Weinberger, New bounds in harmonic and biharmonic problems. Jour. Math. Phys., 33, 1955, 291-307.

339. Peaceman, D. W. and H. H. Rachford, Jr., The numerical solution of parabolic and elliptic differential equations. Jour. Soc. Ind. Appl. Math., 3, 1955, 28-41.

340. Pearson, C. E., A computational method for viscous flow problems. Jour. Fluid Mech., 21, 1965, 611-622.

341. Perron, O., Eine neue Behandlung der Randwertaufgabe fur $\Delta u = 0$. Math. Z., 18, 1923, 42-54.

342. Petrosvky, I. G., New proof of the existence of a solution of Dirichlet's problem by the method of finite differences (Russian). Uspekhi Matem. Nauk, 18, 1941, 161-170.

343. ________, Lectures on partial differential equations. Interscience, New York, 1957.

344. Phillips, H. and N. Wiener, Nets and the Dirichlet problem. Jour. Math. Phys., 2, 1923, 105-124.

345. Picard, E., Memoire sur la theorie des equations aux derivees partielles et la methode des approximations successives. Jour. Math. Pures et Appl., series 4, tome vi, 1890, 145-210.

346. Picone, M., Nuovo metodo d'approssimazione per la soluzione del problema di Dirichlet. Reale Acc. Naz. Lincei, 31, 1922, 357-359.

347. ________, Sul metodo delle minime potenze ponderate e sul metodo di Ritz per il calcolo approssimato nei problemi della fisica matimatica. Rend. Circ. Mat. Palermo, 1928.

348. Plateau, J., Sur les figures d'equilibre d'une masse liquide sans pesanteur. Mem. Acad. Roy. Belgique, N. S., 23, 1849.

349. Pitchaiah, V., Finite difference methods in the solution of Laplace's equation with mixed boundary conditions on a rectangular domain. Ph. D. thesis, U. Minnesota, 1965.

350. Pohozaev, S. T., The Dirichlet problem for the equation $\Delta u = u^2$. Soviet Math., 1, 1960, 1143-1146.

351. ________, On the boundary value problem for the equation $\Delta u = u^2$. Soviet Math., 2, 1961, 609.

352. Polozii, G. N., A numerical method of solving boundary value problems for partial differential equations. Soviet Math., 1, 1960, 1016-1019.

353. Polya, G., Estimating electrostatic capacity. Amer. Math. Mo., 54, 1947, 201-206.

354. Polya, G. and G. Szego, Isoperimetric Inequalities in Mathematical Physics, Princeton Univ. Press, Princeton, N. J., 1951.

355. Prodi, G., Problemi al contorno nonlineari per equazioni di tipo parabolico in due variabili-soluzioni periodiche. Rend. Sem. Mat. Univ. Padova, 23, 1954, 25-85.

356. Rabinowitz, P. H., Periodic solutions of nonlinear hyperbolic partial differential equations. Comm. Pure Appl. Math., 20, 1967, 145-206.

357. Rado, T., On the problem of Plateau. Chelsea, New York, 1951.

358. Rellich, F., Über das asymptotische Verhalten der Lösungen von $\Delta u + \lambda u = 0$ in unendlichen Gebieten. Jahresber. Deutsch. Math.-Verein. 53, 1943, 57-65.

359. Richardson, L. F., The approximate arithmetical solution by finite differences of physical problems involving differential equations with an application to the stresses in a masonry dam. Phil. Trans. Roy. Soc. London, 210A, 1910, 307-357.

360. Richardson, R. G. D., A new method in boundary problems for differential equations. Trans. AMS, 18, 1917, 489-518.

361. Richtmyer, R. D., The stability criterion of Godunov and Ryabenkii for difference schemes. T. I. D. -45, N. Y. O. - 1480-4, AEC Computing and Applied Mathematics Center, New York University, 1964.

362. Rigler, A. K., Estimation of the successive over-relaxation factor. Math. Comp., 19, 1965, 302-307.

363. Riley, J. D., Iteration procedures for the Dirichlet difference problem. MTAC, 1954, 125-131.

364. Rivkind, V. Ya., An approximate method for the solution of the Dirichlet problem and estimates of rates of convergence of the solutions of difference equations to the solutions of elliptic equations with discontinuous coefficients (Russian). Vestn. Leningrad un-ta, Ser. matem., mekhan. i astron., 13, 1964, 37-52.

365. Rosen, J.B., Approximate computational solution of nonlinear parabolic partial differential equations by linear programming, in Numerical solutions of nonlinear differential equations, Wiley, New York, 1966.

366. Rosenbloom, P. C., On the difference equation method for solving the Dirichlet problem. NBS AMS, 18, 1952, 231-237.

367. Rosser, J. B., Block relaxation by computer. Tech. Rpt. 477, Math. Res. Ctr., Madison, Wisconsin, 1964.

368. Roudebush, W. H., Analysis of discretization errors for differential equations with discontinuous coefficients. Ph. D. thesis. Case Institute of Technology, 1963.

369. Rowe, P. P., Difference approximations to partial derivatives for uneven spacings in the network. Trans. Amer. Geophys. Union, 36, 1955, 995-1008.

370. Royster, W. C., A Poisson integral formula for the ellipse and some applications. Proc. AMS, 15, 1964, 661-670.

371. Runge, C., Uber eine Methode die partielle Differentialgleichung Δu = constans numerisch zu integrieren. Zeits. f. Math. u. Phys., 56, 1908-1909, 225-232.

372. ________, Graphische Losung von Randwertaufgaben der Gleichung $\nabla^2 u = 0$. Nach. Gott. Math. Phys. Klasse, 1911, 431-448.

373. Samanskii, V. E., Methods of numerical solution of boundary value problems on ECVM. Part I (Russian). Izdat. Akad. Nauk Ukrain. SSSR, Kiev, 1963.

374. Samarskii, A. A., On monotone difference schemes for elliptic and parabolic equations in the case of a non-self-adjoint elliptic operator (Russian). Z. Vycisl. Mat. i Mat. Fiz., 5, 1965, 548-551.

375. Samarskii, A. A. and V. B. Andreev, A difference scheme of higher accuracy for an equation of elliptic type in several space variables (Russian). Z. Vycisl. Mat. i Mat. Fiz., 3, 1963, 1006-1013.

376. Sapagovas, M. P., Solution of quasilinear elliptic equations by the difference method (Russian). Litovsk. Mat. Sb., 5, 1965, 291-302.

377. Saulev, V. K., An example of an application of S. L. Sobolev's imbedding theorem to numerical mathematics (Russian). Dokl. Akad. Nauk SSSR, 147, 1962, 303-305.

378. ________, Solution of certain boundary value problems on high-speed computers by the fictitious-domain method (Russian). Sibirsk Mat. Z., 4, 1963, 912-925.

379. Schechter, M., On the Dirichlet problem for second order elliptic equations with coefficients singular at the boundary. Comm. Pure Appl. Math., 13, 1960, 321-328.

380. Schechter, S., Relaxation methods for linear equations. Comm. Pure Appl. Math., 12, 1959, 313-335.

381. ________, Iteration methods for nonlinear problems. Trans. AMS, 1962, 179-189.

382. Schneider, E., Uber eine neue Methode zur angenaherten numerischen Integration der Laplaceschen Differentialgleichungen, zugleich ein Beitrag zur Theorie der Torsion. Diss. Jena, Weida i. Thur.: Thomas u Hubert, 50 S. 8°, 1916.

383. Schot, J. W., On the numerical solution of Poisson's equation in an elliptic region. Interim Tech. Rpt. 29, Dept. of Army project 5B99-01-004, Dept. of Math., University of Maryland, 1957.

384. Schroder, J., Zur Losung von Potentialaufgaben mit Hilfe des Differenzenverfahrens. ZAMM, 34, 1954, 241-253.

385. Seget, K., Comparison of the exactness of several formulations of boundary conditions in the use of the finite difference method (Russian). Apl. Mat., 10, 1965, 302-307.

386. Sheldon, J. W., On the numerical solution of elliptic difference equations. MTAC, 1955, 101-112.

387. ________, Algebraic approximations for Laplace's equation in the neighborhood of interfaces. MTAC, 12, 1958, 174-186.

388. Sheldon, J. W. and D. P. Squier, Remarks on the order of convergence of discrete analogs for second-order elliptic partial differential equations. SIAM Rev., vol. 4, no. 4, 1962, 366-378.

389. Shiffman, M., On the existence of subsonic flows of a compressible fluid. Jour. Rat. Mech. and Anal., 1, 1952, 605-652.

390. Shortley, G. H. and R. Weller, The numerical solution of Laplace's equation. Jour. Appl. Phys., 9, 1938, 334-348.

391. Shortley, G. H., R. Weller, P. Darbey, and E. H. Gamble, Numerical solution of axisymmetrical problems, with applications to electrostatics and torsion. Eng. Exp. Sta. Bull. No. 128, Ohio State University, 1947.

392. Shortley, G. H., R. Weller, and B. Fried, Numerical solution of Laplace's and Poisson's equations. Eng. Exp. Sta. Bull. No. 107, Ohio State University, 1940.

393. Shuleshko, P., A method of integration over the boundary for solving boundary value problems. Austral. Jour. Appl. Sci., 12, 1961, 393-406.

394. Slobodyanskii, M. G., Approximate solution of some boundary problems for elliptic differential equations and estimates of the error (Russian). Dokl. Akad. Nauk SSSR (N. S.), 89, 1953, 221-224.

395. ________, Method of approximate integration of differential equations with partial derivatives and its application to problems of elasticity. (Russian). Appl. Math. Mech., Moscow, (2) 3, no. 1, 75-82.

396. Smith, J., The coupled equation approach to the numerical solution of the biharmonic equation by finite differences. Report supported by NASA Sustaining University Program - NGR 43-001-021, Univ. of Tennessee, n. d.

397. Sobrero, L., Un metodo di approssimazioni successive per la risoluzione del problema di Dirichlet. Ann. Scuola Norm. Super. Pisa (3), 3, 1949, 1950, 67-93.

398. Sokolov, G. T., Periodic solutions of the wave equation (Russian). Fergan. Gos. Ped. Inst. Ucen.Zap. Ser. Mat. Vyp. 1, 1965, 17-25.

399. Solomon, A., Systems of minimal surfaces. Comm. Pure Appl. Math., 20, 521-547, 1967.

400. Southwell, R. V., Relaxation methods in engineering science. Oxford Univ. Press, Oxford, England, 1940.

401. Southwell, R. V. and G. Vaisey, Plane potential problems involving specified normal gradients. Proc. Roy. Soc. London, A182, 1943, 129-151.

402. Spinelli, R. A., Poisson equation on a sphere. SIAM Jour. Num.-Anal., 3, 1965, 489-499.

403. Squier, D. P., On the existence and uniqueness of solutions of the Poisson interface problem. Amer. Jour. Math., 85, 1963, 241-247.

404. Stein, P. and J. E. L. Peck, On the numerical solution of Poisson's equation over a rectangle. Pac. Jour. Math., 5, Suppl. II, 1955, 999-1011.

405. Sternberg, W., Die Theorie der Randwertaufgaben im Gebiete der partiellen Differentialgleichungen. Pascal's Repertorium der hoheren Mathematic, 1, part 3, Teubner, Leipzig, 1929, 1121-1139.

406. Sternberg, W. and T. I. Smith, The theory of potential and spherical harmonics. Univ. Toronto Press, Toronto, Canada, 1946.

407. Stetter, H. J., On the convergence of characteristic finite-difference methods of high accuracy for quasilinear hyperbolic equations. Num. Math., 3, 1961, 321-344.

408. Stiefel, E., La machina a calculer arithmetique "Z4" de l'Ecole Polytechnique Federale a Zurich (Suisse) et son application a la resolution d'une equation aux derivees partielles de type elliptique. Centre Nat. Rech. Sci., Paris, colloq. no. 37, 1953.

409. Stognii, A. A., Finding a series solution to the Laplace equation on an electronic digital computer (Russian). Vopr. vychisl. matem. i vychisl. tekhn. M., Mashgiz, 1963, 55-58.

410. Strang, W. G., Difference methods for mixed boundary-value problems. Duke Math. Jour., 27, 1960, 221-232.

411. Stresneva, V. A., Auxiliary tables for the solution of Poisson's equation for polygonal regions by the method of reduction to ordinary differential equations (Russian). Trudy Mat. Inst. Steklov, 53, 1959, 267-282.

412. Struik, D. J., Lectures on classical differential geometry, Addison Wesley, Reading, Mass., 1950.

413. Sugai, I., Numerical solution of Laplace's equation given Cauchy conditions. I. B. M. Jour. Res. Dev., 3, 1959, 187-188.

414. Sulhanisvili, G. I., On the numerical solution of the generalized nonhomogeneous polyharmonic equation (Russian). Soobsc. Akad. Nauk Gruzin. SSSR, 31, 1963, 3-8.

415. Sunatani, C. and S. Negoro, On a method of approximate solution of a plane harmonic function. Trans. Soc. Mech. Eng., Tokyo, 3, 1937, 6-11.

416. Synge, J. L., The hypercircle in mathematical physics. Cambridge Univ. Press, Cambridge, England, 1957

417. Taylor, G. I. and C. F. Sherman, A mechanical method for solving problems of flow in compressible fluids. Proc. Roy. Soc., A. 121, 1928, 194-217.

418. Tee, G. J., A new technique for solving elliptic partial differential equations. Jour. SIAM, 12, 1964, 311-347.

419. Thomeé, V., Elliptic difference operators and Dirichlet's problem. Tech. note BN-345, Inst. Fluid Dyn. Appl. Math., College Park, Maryland, 1964.

420. Thuraisamy, V., Discrete analogs for mixed boundary value problems of elliptic type. Tech. Rpt. BN-506, Univ. Maryland, Coll. Pk., Md., 1967.

421. Todd, J., Experiments in the solution of differential equations by Monte Carlo methods. Jour. Wash. Acad. Sci., vol. 44, no. 12, 1954, 377-381.

422. Todd, J. (editor), Survey of numerical methods. McGraw-Hill, New York, 1962.

423. Tranter, C. J., The combined use of relaxation methods and Fourier transforms in the solution of some three-dimensional boundary value problems. Quart. Jour. Mech. Appl. Math., 1, 1948, 281-286.

424. Trytten, G. N., Pointwise bounds for solutions of the Cauchy problem for elliptic equations. NOL TR 62-91, Naval Ord. Lab., White Oak, Maryland, 1962.

425. Uhlmann, W., Differenzenverfahren fur die 2 and 3 Randwertaufgabe mit krummlinigen Randern bei $\Delta u(x, y) = r(x, y, u)$. ZAMM, 38, 1958, 226-251.

426. ________, Uber harmonische und isotrope stochastische Prozesse mit Fehlerschatzung fur ein Differenzenverfahren. ZAMM, 41, 1961, 428-447.

427. ________, Uber den Fehler bei Differenzenverfahren fur die Poissonsche Differentialgleichung. Num. Mat., 4, 1962, 226-237.

428. Varga, R. S., Matrix iterative analysis. Prentice-Hall, Englewood Cliffs, New Jersey, 1962.

429. Vekua, I. N., A boundary problem with oblique derivative for an equation of elliptic type (Russian). Dokl. Akad. Nauk SSSR (N. S.), 92, 1953, 1113-1116.

430. Visik, M. I. and O. A. Ladyzenskaya, Boundary value problems for partial differential equations and certain classes of operator equations. AMS Translations, series 2, vol. 10, 223-282.

431. Viswanathan, R. V., Solution of Poisson's equation by relaxation method: normal gradient specified on curved boundaries. MTAC, 11, 1957, 67-78.

432. Vlasov, V. K. and A. B. Bakusinskii, The method of potentials and the numerical solution of the Dirichlet problem for the Laplace equation (Russian). Z. Vycisl. Mat. i Mat. Fiz., 3, 1963, 574-580.

433. Vlasova, Z. A., A numerical realization of the method of reduction to ordinary differential equations (Russian). Sibirsk. Mat. Z., 4, 1963, 475-479.

434. ________, The grid method for a nonlinear one-dimensional variational problem. Trudy Mat. Inst. Steklov, 66, 1962, 196-204.

435. Volkov, E. A., On a solution by the method of grids of equations of elliptic type with boundary conditions containing derivatives (Russian). Dokl. Akad. Nauk SSSR (N. S.), 102, 1955, 437-440.

436. ________, On the solution by the method of nets of the interior Dirichlet problem for the Laplace equation (Russian). Vycisl. Mat., 1, 1957, 34-61.

437. ________, Investigation of a method for increasing the accuracy of the net method for the solution of Poisson's equation (Russian). Vycisl. Mat., 1, 1957, 62-80.

438. ________, The method of nets for boundary value problems with skew and normal derivatives (Russian). Z. Vycisl. Mat. i Mat. Fiz., 1, 1961, 607-621.

439. ________, Application of the Lagrange interpolation polynomial for solving the Dirichlet problem for the Poisson equation by the method of nets (Russian). Z. Vycisl. Mat. i Mat. Fiz. 4, 1964, 466-472.

440. ________, Effective error bounds by the method of nets for solutions of the Dirichlet problem for the Laplace equation on polygons (Russian). Dokl. Akad. Nauk SSSR, 155, 1964, 735-738.

441. ________, Solution of the Dirichlet problem by refinement with higher order differences. Dokl. Akad. Nauk SSSR, 164, 1965, 479-482.

442. ________, The lack of basis for Batschelet's majorant method and an estimate of the error in the solution of the mixed boundary value problem by the mesh method. USSR Comp. Math. and Math. Phys., 5, 1965.

443. Volkov , E. A. , The method of nets for the exterior Dirichlet problem (Russian). Z. Vycisl. Mat. i Mat. Fiz., 6, 1966, 503-511.

444. von Mises, R. , Mathematical theory of compressible fluid flow. Academic Press, New York, 1959.

445. Voytuk, J. A. and R. C. MacCamy, Mixed boundary value problems in the plane. Proc. AMS, 16, 1965, 276-280.

446. Vzorova, A. I. , Tables for the solution of Laplace's equation on an elliptic region (Russian). Academy of Science, Moscow, 1957.

447. Wachspress, E. L. , The numerical solution of boundary value problems. Mathematical Methods for Digital Computers, Wiley, New York, 1960, 121-127.

448. ________, Iterative solution of elliptic systems and applications to the neutron diffusion equations of reactor physics. Prentice Hall, Englewood Cliffs, N. J. , 1966.

449. Walker, M. S. , Iterative methods for the solution of elliptic partial differential equations. Associateship thesis, Royal College of Science and Technology, Glasgow, 1961.

450. Walsh, J. L. , Solution of the Dirichlet problem for the ellipse by interpolating harmonic polynomials. Jour. Math. Mech. 9, 1960, 193-196.

451. Walsh, J. L. and D. Young, On the accuracy of the numerical solution of the Dirichlet problem by finite differences. Jour. Res. Nat. Bur. Stand., vol. 51, no. 6, 1953, 343-363.

452. ________, On the degree of convergence of solutions of difference equations to the solution of the Dirichlet problem. Jour. Math. Phys., 33, 1954, 80-93.

453. ________, Lipschitz conditions for harmonic and discrete harmonic functions. Jour. Math. Phys., vol. 36, no. 2, 1957, 138-150.

454. Warschawski, S. E. , Recent results in numerical methods of conformal mapping. Proc. Symp. Appl. Math., AMS, vol. 6, 1956.

455. Warten, R. M. , On the approximate solution of axially symmetric problems by means of finite differences. Ph. D. thesis, Purdue University, August, 1961.

456. Waschakidze, D., On the numerical solution of the biharmonic equation (Russian). Tbliss. Mat. Inst. Trudy, 9, 1941, 61-73.

457. Wasow, W., Random walks and the eigenvalues of elliptic difference equations. Jour. Res. Nat. Bur. Stand., vol. 46, no. 1, 1951, 65-73.

458. ________, On the truncation error in the solution of Laplace's equation by finite differences. Jour. Res. Nat. Bur. Stand., 48, 1952, 345-348.

459. ________, Discrete approximations to elliptic differential equations. ZAMP, 6, 1955, 81-97.

460. ________, The accuracy of difference approximations to plane Dirichlet problems with piecewise analytic boundary values. Quart. Appl. Math., 15, 1957, 53-63.

461. Weinberger, H. F., Upper and lower bounds for eigenvalues by finite difference methods. Comm. Pure Appl. Math., 9, 1956, 613-623.

462. ________, Exact information by finite difference approximation. Tech. Note BN-173, Inst. Fluid Dynamics and Applied Math., College Park, Maryland, 1959.

463. Weinstein, A., Generalized axially symmetric potential theory. Bull. AMS, 59, 1953, 20-38.

464. ________, Singular partial differential equations and their applications. Proc. Symp. Fluid Dyn. and Appl. Math. at Univ. Md., 1961; Gordon and Breach, New York, 1963, 29-49.

465. Weinstock, R., Calculus of variations, McGraw-Hill, New York, 1952.

466. Weller, R., G. H. Shortly, and B. Fried, Solution of torsion problems by numerical integration of Poisson's equation. Jour. Appl. Phys., 11, 283-290.

467. Whitehead, S., An approximate solution for the distribution of temperature or potential with cylindrical isothermal or equipotential surfaces. Proc. Phys. Soc. Lond., 54, 63-65.

468. Wigley, N. M., On the convergence of discrete approximations to solutions of mixed boundary value problems. SIAM Jour. Num. Anal., 3, 1966, 372-382.

469. Wilcox, C. H., Regularity theorems for solutions of initial-boundary value problems for linear hyperbolic equations of the second order. Tech. Rpt. 533, Math. Res. Ctr., U. Wis., Madison, Wis., 1964.

470. Williams, W. E., Approximate solution of boundary value problems in potential theory with applications to electrostatics and elastostatics. Proc. Edin. Math. Soc., 14, 1964, 89-101.

471. Wilson, W. L., On discrete Dirichlet and Plateau problems. Num. Mat., 3, 1961, 359-373.

472. Windsor, E., Iterative solutions of biharmonic differential equations. Master's thesis, N. Y. U., 1957.

473. Wise, H. and C. M. Ablow, Diffusion and heterogeneous reaction, IV. Jour. Chem. Phys., 35, 1961, 10-18.

474. Wolf, F., Uber die angenaherte numerische Berechnung harmonischer und biharmonischer Funktionen. ZAMM, 6, 1926, 118-150.

475. Woods, L. C., The relaxation treatment of singular points in Poisson's equation. Quart. Jour. Mech. Appl. Math., 6, 1953, 163-185.

476. Young, D., Iterative methods for solving partial difference equations of elliptic type. Trans. AMS, 76, 1954, 92-111.

477. ________, ORDVAC solutions of the Dirichlet problem. Jour. Assoc. Computing Machinery, 2, 1955, 137-161.

478. ________, The numerical solution of elliptic and parabolic partial differential equations. Survey of Numerical Analysis, McGraw-Hill, New York, 1962, 380-438.

479. Young, D. and H. Shaw, ORDVAC solutions of $\frac{\partial^2 u}{\partial x^2} + \frac{\partial^2 u}{\partial y^2} + \frac{k}{y}\frac{\partial u}{\partial y} = 0$ for boundary value problems and problems of mixed type. Interim Tech. Rpt. No. 14, U. S. Army Contract DA-36-034-ORD-1486. Mathematics Dept., Univ. Maryland, College Park, Maryland, 1955.

480. Young, D. and C. H. Warlick, On the use of Richardson's method for the numerical solution of Laplace's equation on the ORDVAC. Ballistic Res. Labs. Rpt. 707, Aberdeen Proving Grounds, Maryland, 1953.

481. Young, J. D., Application of linear programming to the solution of linear differential equations. Univ. Cal., Lawrence Rad. Lab., Berkeley, Cal., UCRL-10110, March 1, 1962.

482. Zachmanoglou, E. C., The decay of solutions of the initial-boundary value problem for hyperbolic equations. Jour. Math. Anal. Appl., 13, 1966, 504-515.

483. Zaremba, S., Sur le calcul numerique des fonctions demandees dans le probleme de Dirichlet et le probleme hydrodynamique. International de l'Academie des Science de Cracovie, Bulletin, 1909, 125-195.

484. Zhileikin, Ya. M., An approximate solution of the Dirichlet problem for Laplace's equation (Russian). Dokl. AN SSSR, 155, 1964, 999-1002.

485. Zolin, A. F., Solution of boundary value problems for the Laplace equation by an interpolation method (Russian). Issled. po Mat. Analizii i Mehanike v Uzbekistane, Izdat. Akad. Nauk Uzbek. SSR, Tashkent, 1960, 133-152.

486. ________, On an approximate solution of boundary value problems for equations of elliptic type (Russian). Proc. First Sci. Conf. Math. Dept. Ped. Inst. Volga Region, Kuybyshev Gos. Ped. Inst., Kuybyshev, 1961, 61-65.